P9-CQH-845

HarperCollinsPublishersLtd

Published in the United States by Joe Books
Publisher: Adam Fortier
President: Jody Colero
CEO: Jay Firestone
567 Queen St W, Toronto, ON M5V 2B6
www.joebooks.com

HarperCollins Books may be purchased for educational, business, or sales promotional use through our Special Markets Department.

HarperCollins Publishers Ltd
2 Bloor Street East, 20th Floor
Toronto, Ontario, Canada
M4W 1A8

www.harpercollins.ca

Library and Archives Canada Cataloguing in Publication information is available upon request.

ISBN 978-1-443442-83-1 (HarperCollins Publishers Ltd edition, Canada)
ISBN 978-1-926516-00-4 (Joe Books edition, US)
First Joe Books and HarperCollins Publishers Ltd Editions: November 2014
3 5 7 9 10 8 6 4 2

Published in the United States by Joe Books, Inc.
Published in Canada by HarperCollins Publishers Ltd, by arrangement with Joe Books, Inc.

Printed in USA through Avenue4 Communications at Cenveo/Richmond, Virginia

For information regarding the CPSIA on this printed material, call: (203) 595-3636 and provide reference #RICH - 592792.

ADAPTED BY: ROBERT SIMPSON, ERIK BURNHAM AND JOSH ELDER
INTRODUCTION BY LEONARD MALTIN
COVER ART BY THE DISNEY STUDIOS
LETTERING AND LAYOUT:
SALVADOR NAVARRO, EDUARDO ALPUENTE, ALBERTO GARRIDO
DESIGNER: ERIKA TERRIQUEZ

SENIOR EDITOR: CAROLYNN PRIOR
EDITOR: ROBERT SIMPSON
PRODUCTION COORDINATOR: STEPHANIE ALOUCHE

SPECIAL THANKS TO:
STEVE OSGOODE, TONYA AGURTO, DANIEL SAEVA, CURT BAKER,
LEONARD MALTIN AND EDDY COLERO.

Disney

FROZEN

BEHIND THE SCENES

BY LEONARD MALTIN

Some movies are flops, others are hits, while a select few go well beyond box-office success and make a marked impact on our culture. Released toward the end of 2013, *Frozen* has had that effect on audiences of all ages and nationalities.

The film's success is exemplified by the enormous popularity of its signature anthem, "Let It Go," which propelled a Platinum-selling soundtrack, inspired countless performances on YouTube, and earned an Academy Award as Best Original Song. *Frozen* also made history by winning an Academy Award for Best Animated Feature, the first time a Walt Disney Animated Studio film has won in that category.

Whether you're a casual admirer or a devotee, I think you'll enjoy experiencing the movie in graphic novel style. It's an entirely new way of integrating the story, dialogue, and visuals from a movie into the realm of the comic book. It also derives inspiration from

Walt Disney's great legacy in the world of comics, which included adaptations of the studio's animated and live-action features in the 1950s and 60s.

Critics and pundits have tried to analyze why this film has resonated so strongly with moviegoers young and old, male and female. Is it that there are *two* princess heroines—or that so many people can relate to a troubled sibling relationship? Is it because the princesses are flawed? Is it the endearing comedic relief of Olaf the snowman and Sven the reindeer, or the contemporary quality of the songs?

"After having been around Disney for a long time, I wanted to do something different," says Chris Buck, co-director of *Frozen*. "Can true love be something other than the male lead's kiss? I was playing with the idea of true love versus romantic love."

Of course, that serious theme is woven into a colorful and dynamic fabric of music, humor, imagination, and often stunning imagery.

In truth, there is no way to quantify *Frozen*'s popularity. If there were a formula for creating megahit movies, everyone would follow it and there would be no failures. Something set this film apart, and that "something" is probably the sum of its many parts.

Yet just as *Snow White* was a film of its time, and *The Little Mermaid* reflected a later generation, *Frozen* is unquestionably a product of the

21st century…and the sensibilities of a female writer-director. There is no question that a modern woman like Jennifer Lee (who joined Disney in 2011, to work on the screenplay of *Wreck-It Ralph*) would have a different approach to both the male and female characters in a film of this kind. *Frozen* represents a healthy collaboration between Lee and her co-director, Disney veteran Chris Buck.

Gone is the practically perfect heroine, replaced by two sisters whose childhood friendship is ruptured by a cruel twist of fate. Elsa has magical powers that she can't control. Anna, shut out by her sibling and never knowing why, grows up to be a spunky, awkward but caring young woman with a true sense of wonder. With her spirited, optimistic, and fearless manner, she could never be mistaken for the simple, pure-hearted Snow White.

Lee says she wanted to create a heroine she could relate to. "I talk too fast, I'm messy, I'm sloppy, I'm goofy, I'm weird. We just felt like we could do that."

Asked if they were consciously trying to modernize the classical Disney fairy tale, Buck responds, "We are a product of our environment and our society, and that's what we put up on the screen."

Frozen also features not one but two heroes: one, a traditionally handsome prince named Hans who sweeps the naïve, unworldly Anna off her feet; and Kristoff, a mountain man who's so unaccustomed to dealing with people that he holds two-way conversations with his reindeer, providing Sven's dialogue as well as his own. (This subversion of the classical hero was first tried out in Disney's *Beauty and the Beast*, which sent a message to audiences, and its leading lady, that one shouldn't judge a book by its cover. Or to put it another way, a handsome hunk isn't always a hero.)

The foundation of any Disney animated feature is the story. Unlike a live-action screenplay, this is rarely the work of one writer but instead a team effort, wrestled to life through constant exploration and endless revisions. Experience is the best teacher in this process. Although Jennifer Lee is a relative newcomer to the studio, her work on *Wreck-It Ralph* was her baptism of fire. This is also the second Disney venture for composer-lyricists Kristin Anderson-Lopez and Robert Lopez, who contributed charming songs to the studio's 2011 feature *Winnie the Pooh*. Chris Buck has the longest Disney résumé, having started at the studio in 1978 and worked as an animator and character designer on a variety of projects before directing *Tarzan* (with Kevin Lima).

It surely didn't hurt to have the input of executive producer John Lasseter, the co-founder of Pixar, whose own studio emphasizes the importance of story construction just as Walt Disney did.

Although the movie takes its inspiration from Hans Christian Andersen's famous fairy tale, written in 1845, it bears scant resemblance to the original. *The Snow Queen* is the Danish writer's longest work, consisting of seven loosely connected vignettes. Each segment introduces new characters, settings, and motifs. (This hasn't stopped anyone from adapting it for stage, screen, and even ballet; there have been countless productions of *The Snow Queen* over the years, in many countries.) Boiled down to basics: Devoted young friends Kai and Gerda are separated when the evil Snow Queen abducts Kai, whose personality undergoes a dark transformation

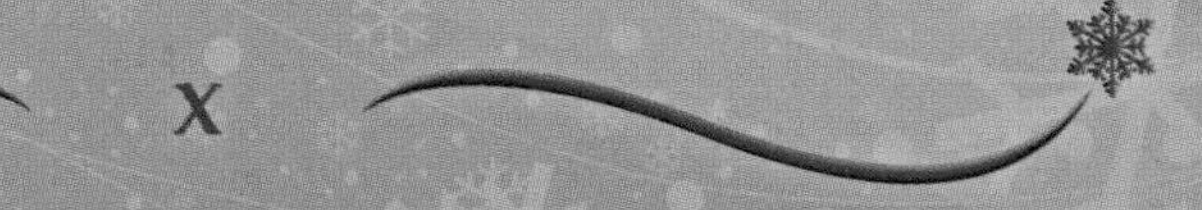

because a piece of a troll mirror that only reflects negative qualities in people lodges in his eyes and his heart. Gerda sets out on an arduous journey to find her missing friend and tracks him to the Snow Queen's palace.

There are no royal sisters, no talking snowman or friendly reindeer. A kingdom isn't frozen and there aren't two men vying for a princess' favor. All of this was generated from scratch by the film's creative team, although Buck says, "We were inspired by that struggle and appreciated the overall message Andersen is sharing. We were also drawn to Gerda, the girl in the story who wants to save Kai. Her core characteristics— optimism, love, strength and determination—began to form what would become Anna."

Another component in the creation of three-dimensional characters is casting. The right actors bring a great deal to their vocal performances and inspire the animators and story team. Kristen Bell and Idina Menzel were ideal choices to portray the grown-up Anna and Elsa, because they are talented actresses as well as singers.

In the case of Olaf, the filmmakers were still grappling with how to portray the snowman when they met with Broadway performer Josh Gad, who won acclaim for his work in such hit musicals as *The 25th Annual Putnam County Spelling Bee* and *The Book of Mormon*.

Lee told me, "We were searching for the Olaf voice, and I couldn't write him. I knew he represented innocent love, but I couldn't feel how he would speak. Then Josh became available, and he came in one day. I brought in three pages; he did them, and then we played. We improv'ed and we talked and we explored. That session is the 'meet Olaf' scene, exactly; it was from that session. Then I knew him, and I could write him. It was so much fun and so easy." (Songwriter

Robert Lopez already knew Gad from having worked with him on *Mormon*.)

In some cases, songs helped express story points and character motivations better than dialogue could. The composers came up with the song "Let It Go" early on, to represent Elsa breaking free from years of repressed emotions. The filmmakers loved it, but it made them rethink scenes leading up to the moment.

"'Let It Go' was the first song that we all knew belonged in the film because it helped shape Elsa's character," says Lee. "It delivers such a poignant and powerful message about how she's feeling that we needed to back up and earn that song—to show how she finds herself in that place at that time."

The songwriting team of Anderson-Lopez and Lopez brought a modern-day mindset to this project that sets it apart from the songs of earlier Disney films. Their lyrics speak in the vernacular of today ("For the First Time in Forever") and the soundtrack's popularity is testament to their vitality.

With story and songs developing, the look of the film must be determined. Here again, many individuals are involved. Knowing that the make-believe kingdom of Arendelle is rooted in Hans Christian Andersen's Scandinavia, art director Mike Giaimo started doing visual research and found that he was drawn (no pun intended) to the look of Norway.

"We wanted to create an intimate world with an enchanting and dynamic setting that would be immediately identifiable for

generations to come," he says. "Norway offered a cultural backdrop we'd never explored before, and we thought, 'Wouldn't it be great to blend its dramatic natural environment, architecture and folk costume aesthetic?' It feels like a world from a classic Disney film, but it's completely new."

So it was that a group of Disney artists traveled to Norway to soak up atmosphere and fill their sketchpads. They visited villages and castles, fjords and glaciers. No detail was too small: they diligently researched hairstyles and costumes as well as settings. (They even brought back a CD of traditional Norwegian chanting—called "yoiking"—that became the compelling musical performance that opens the film and establishes the setting.)

But it would take more than artists' renderings to enable the movie's characters to interact with snow and ice in a completely credible fashion. The Disney staff did hands-on research to learn about footprints in deep and shallow snow, and how much of the fluffy white stuff would cling to a long skirt. To implement their findings in the production process, the studio's software engineers and visual effects supervisors fashioned brand-new, proprietary tools and technologies. An expert on snow from the California Institute of Technology was called in to advise filmmakers. That research helped the *Frozen* crew craft more than 2,000 individual snowflake designs.

Ice has its own unique visual qualities. It couldn't look like glass or plastic, and had to reflect light as ice actually does. The most difficult element in the film was the Ice Palace.

"For one single shot in which Elsa builds her palace, 50 people worked on the technology required to execute that shot," says Lee.

"And the shot is so complex that just one frame takes 30 hours to render."

It's a long way from the 1935 cartoon *On Ice*, in which Disney animators put Mickey and Minnie Mouse and their pals into a wintry setting: a much simpler task in those days before computer graphics and the audience's expectation of thoroughly realistic backdrops.

Perhaps the most impressive aspect of creating a film like *Frozen* is the way it combines so many ingredients: story and character development, dramatic staging, costume design, settings, visual effects, songs and background music, casting, editing, and more. When it works, it all blends into a seamless whole.

One reason it works so well is an update of Walt Disney's storytelling formula that came about at the time of *The Little Mermaid*. That's when a new team decided to approach each animated film as if it were a Broadway musical. Small wonder that producer Peter Del Vecho, songwriters Kristen Anderson-Lopez and Robert Lopez, and many of the principal voice actors have a solid background in musical theater.

Another reason is the continuity that exists at Disney. Director Chris Buck studied at California Institute of the Arts and, in his earliest days at the studio, learned lifelong lessons from one of Walt's fabled "nine old men," Eric Larson (as did John Lasseter).

There is even a link of continuity for the composer of *Frozen*'s dramatic score, the talented Christophe Beck. While attending the highly regarded film scoring program at USC in Los Angeles, Beck

got his first job on the recommendation of the head of the music department, Buddy Baker. Baker spent many years at the Disney studio as a staff composer and arranger, and provided the score for *The Fox and the Hound*—the first film Chris Buck worked on at Disney.

It may be intangible, but having such ties to Disney history can't be ignored or underestimated. Having people with this background working alongside fresh, new talent—unencumbered by tradition—breeds a healthy, creative atmosphere that offers audiences the best of both worlds.

Ultimately, that may be the real secret of *Frozen*'s success: presenting a classical fairy-tale story with a contemporary point of view.

Welcome to Arendelle

Anna

"I'll bring her back and I'll make this right"

Optimistic, loving and **adorable**, Anna finds **wonder** and **loveliness** in everything. She always sees the glass as half full. She's a true **daydreamer** – and sometimes she gets into **trouble** for that. When Anna and her sister Elsa were kids, they used to be very close: they played together all the time, but one day Elsa locked her out without any explanation – closing the door of her room and of **her heart**. From that moment on, Anna's desire is to reconnect with her sister: she wants Elsa to open the door to her, and wants to be worthy of her sister's love.

Elsa

"I never knew what I was capable of"

Elsa is the heir to the throne of Arendelle. She's a **natural leader**, she's **controlled**, **regal** and **graceful**: everybody in the kingdom loves her. But she has a **dark secret**, a secret she hides even from her sister Anna. Elsa has the **power** to **create ice** and **snow** with her hands, but she's not able to control it at all times. She needs to wear **gloves** most of the time, otherwise she'd **freeze anything she touches**. That's why she shut Anna out – to protect Anna from her powers. She'll soon learn, though, how important it is to open your heart and let the ones that love you in.

Kristoff

"Doesn't sound like true love."

Together with his reindeer – and **best friend** – Sven, Kristoff gets blocks of ice from the **North Mountain** and takes them to Arendelle on his sledge to sell. He spends a lot of time outside and he enjoys his work. Kristoff deeply believes that sooner or later **people always end up hurting you**, so he avoids getting close to anyone – even to the love of his life. Anna asks his help to meet up with her sister Elsa. Two people in the whole kingdom could not be more different...

Sven

Sven and Kristoff have been **inseparable life companions** since they were little. This friendly reindeer is crazy for carrots, and would do anything for his human friend. Although he cannot speak, Kristoff speaks for the two of them, often putting words from his own conscience into the animal's mouth.

Olaf

"Some people are worth melting for"

Olaf is the live version of the first snowman Elsa made when she was still a little girl. **Trusting, curious** and **always excited about the world,** Olaf has a **big heart** and is always ready to help others no matter what. Due to his **magical nature,** Olaf can divide his body into pieces – each of them moving independently – and easily put himself back together. **His greatest dream is to see summer**: he has no idea that heat could melt him!

Marshmallow

"Go away!"

Made by Elsa and prepared to **defend her ice castle**, Marshmallow is a **huge snowman** who is not very friendly towards unwanted visitors – his duty is to push away anyone who dares to get close to his creator. This is an easy task for him because of his **strength**, **agility** and his **terrible ice claws**.

Hans

"I would never shut you out"

Prince Hans of the Southern Isles is **fascinating**, **elegant** and **fun**. Last of thirteen brothers, he meets Anna on the day of Elsa's coronation. The young princess immediately **falls for his smile** and his **charming ways**: it is love at first sight!

FROZEN

DIRECTED BY
CHRIS BUCK
JENNIFER LEE

STORY INSPIRED BY
"THE SNOW QUEEN"
BY HANS CHRISTIAN ANDERSEN
STORY BY
CHRIS BUCK
JENNIFER LEE
SHANE MORRIS

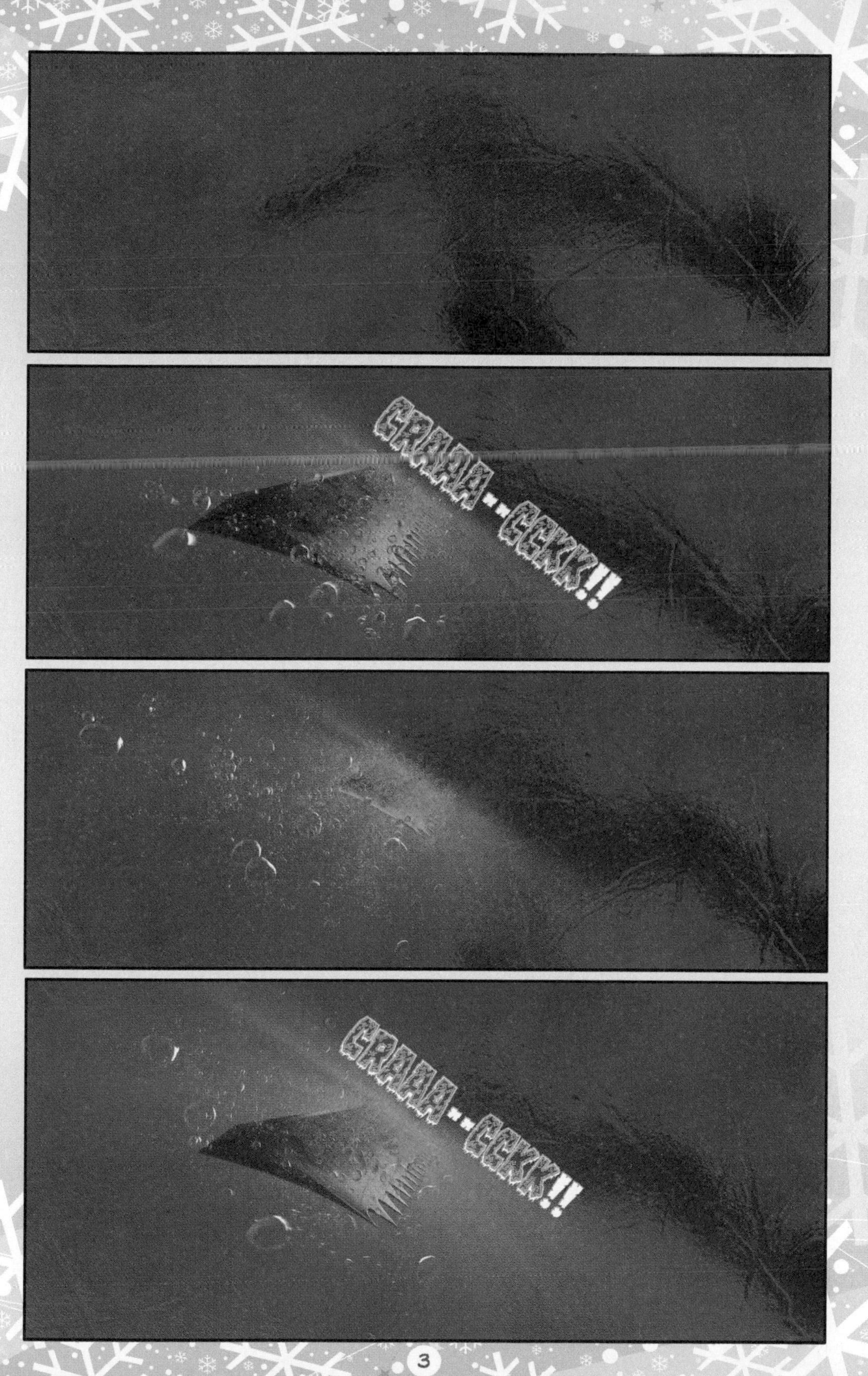
CRAAA--CCKK!!
CRAAA--CCKK!!

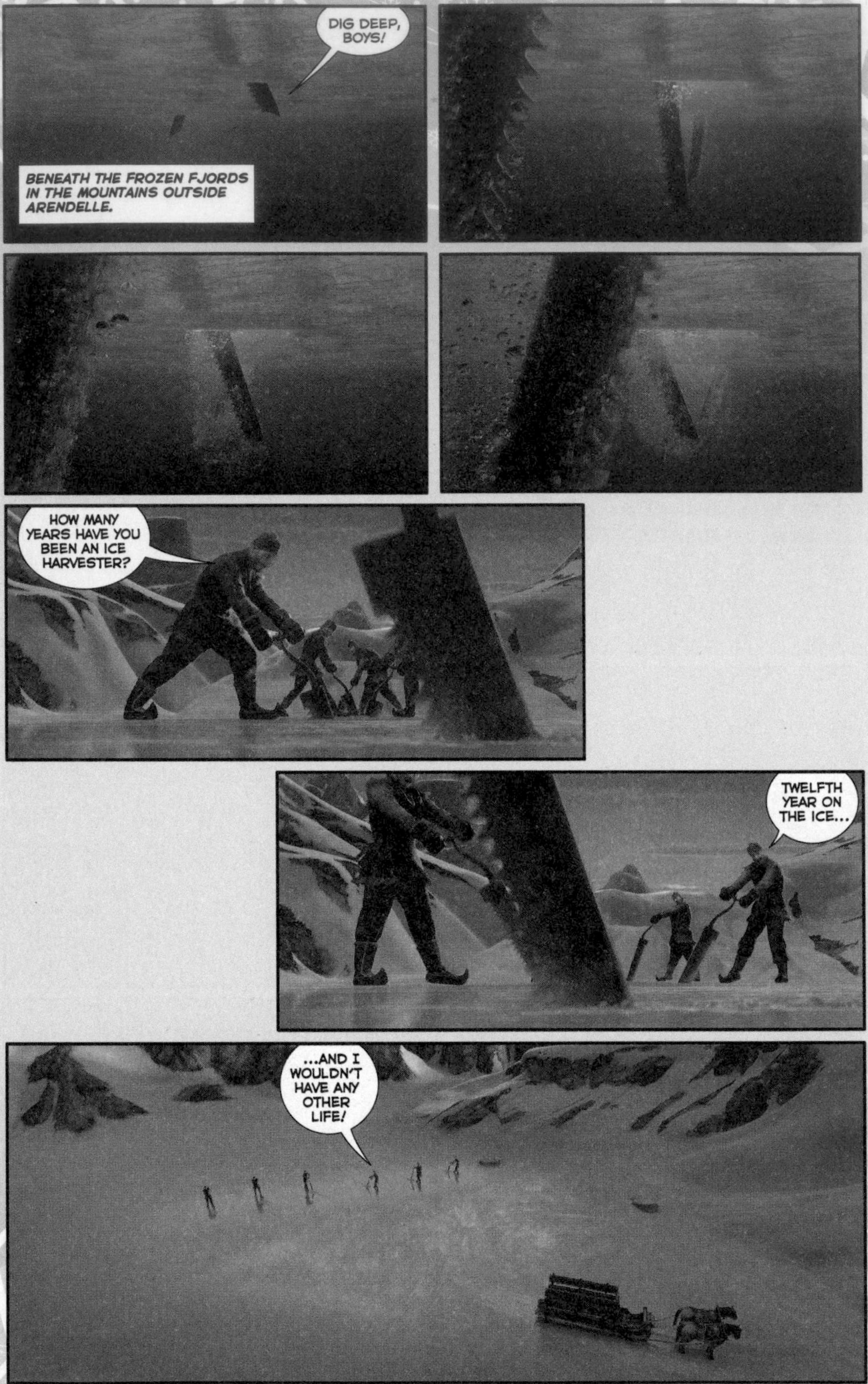

DIG DEEP, BOYS!

BENEATH THE FROZEN FJORDS IN THE MOUNTAINS OUTSIDE ARENDELLE.

HOW MANY YEARS HAVE YOU BEEN AN ICE HARVESTER?

WHAT MADE YOU BECOME AN ICE HARVESTER?
MY FATHER WAS A HARVESTER, HIS FATHER BEFORE HIM, AND HIS FATHER BEFORE HIM...

...AND I WANT TO MAKE MY FATHER PROUD.

WELL, WATCH YOUR FOOTING! WARM WATER CURRENTS CAN WEAKEN ICE RIGHT UNDER YOUR FEET.

ONCE YOU'VE CUT A BLOCK YOU WANT TO GET A GOOD GRIP --

-- AND CRACK IT LOOSE BEFORE THE FRIGID WATERS CAN FREEZE IT AGAIN.

ALL TOGETHER NOW -- HEAVE HO!

REMEMBER -- YOU JUST NEED TO GET IT TO THE NEXT MAN ON THE LINE

GRAB IT AND GIVE IT A GOOD SHOVE!

THAT'S IT -- GRAB AND SHOVE! GRAB AND SHOVE!

HUNGRY, SVEN?

HARVESTING ICE IS HUNGRY WORK!

UNGHH!
-- LIKE SPLITTING A DIAMOND!
CRAA-CCK!

CUTTING THE ICE AND SENDING IT DOWNSTREAM -- THAT'S ONLY HALF THE JOB!

TO GET PAID WE HAVE TO GET THE ICE OUT OF THE WATER!

KRISTOFF! STILL TRYING TO GET YOUR FIRST ICE BLOCK?
HA HA HA!

COME ON, SVEN!

OK, MEN, ALL TOGETHER. FEET APART!
FEET APART!

KNEES BENT!
KNEES BENT!

PUSH DOWN AND THE WATER WILL FORCE THE BLOCK OUT OF THE WATER!

YOUW!

IT WILL BE GOOD TO GO HOME TO ARENDELLE. WE'VE BEEN AWAY TOO LONG.
FEELS LIKE FOREVER.
DO YOU HAVE THE SAW BLADES STRAPPED ON THOSE HORSES YET?
JUST GOT THE LAST ONE RIGGED -- THIS SHOULD SPEED UP THE CUTTING!
HI-YAHH!
WATCH WHERE YOU DRAG THOSE SAWS!
HI-YAHH!
READY, MEN? ON THREE! ONE, TWO --
-- THREE!
CRAA-CCK!

FEET APART, KNEES BENT!
PUSH DOWN ON THE BLOCK...
...AND THE WATER WILL DO THE REST -- !
OK, OK -- ONE MORE TIME!

HAS THERE EVER BEEN A YEAR WITH NO ICE?

NOT AS LONG AS I CAN REMEMBER.

THAT WAGON IS ALMOST FULL -- BRING IN THE NEXT ONE!

FOREMAN! CAN YOU GIVE US A LITTLE LIGHT?

I CAN BARELY SEE THREE FEET IN FRONT OF ME.

HOLD ON -- I HAVE MATCHES HERE SOMEWHERE...

SUN'S RUN OFF TO HIDE, BOYS! PICK UP THE PACE!
FISHING SHIPS WILL BE IN PORT SOON!
WITHOUT THESE BLOCKS--
--ALL THE FISH WILL GO BAD BEFORE THEY MAKE IT TO MARKET!
A FEW MORE BLOCKS AND THAT LAST WAGON SHOULD BE FILLED!
KNEES BENT, FEET APART!
HUP HOOOO-OO
WHOA-A-A!
SNORT!
WE DID IT, SVEN!

BE SURE TO TIE THOSE OFF GOOD AND TIGHT!
ONE QUICK TURN ON A HILLSIDE AND ALL THESE BLOCKS COULD BE AT THE BOTTOM OF A GORGE!
DON'T WORRY -- I'VE BEEN TYING KNOTS SINCE I WAS A BOY!
NOTHING'S COMING LOOSE ON THIS WAGON! NOW SWING THAT BLOCK -- THAT'S IT!
HMPH! WORRYING ABOUT MY KNOTS! HAH!

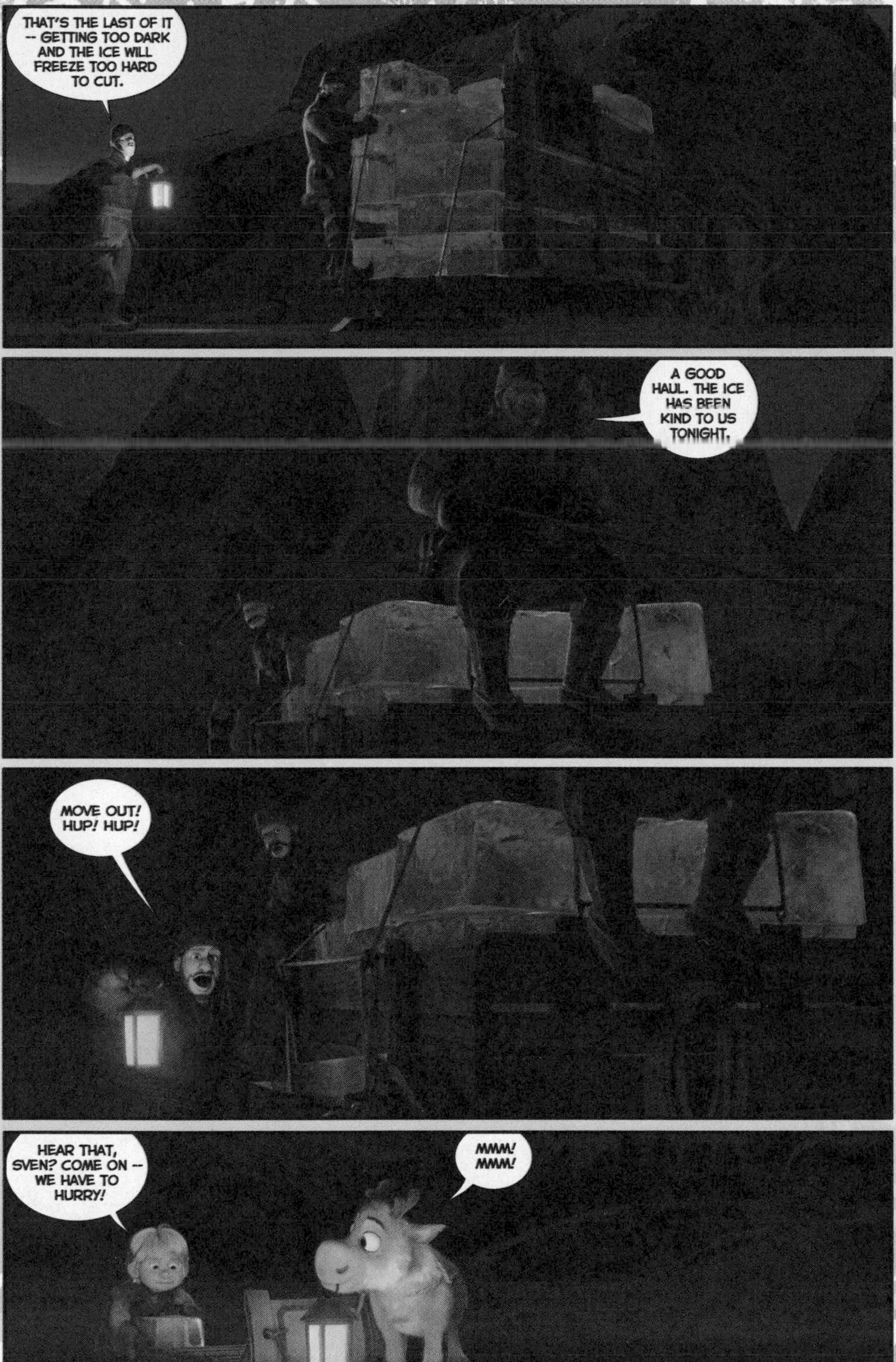

THAT'S THE LAST OF IT -- GETTING TOO DARK AND THE ICE WILL FREEZE TOO HARD TO CUT.

A GOOD HAUL. THE ICE HAS BEEN KIND TO US TONIGHT.

WE'LL SHOW THEM, SVEN--

-- SOMEDAY WE'LL BE THE GREATEST ICE HARVESTERS EVER!

WAIT FOR US! WE'RE COMING!

HII-YAAH! NEXT STOP: ARENDELLE!

THE ICE HARVESTER'S SONG CARRIES ACROSS THE HILLS AND MOUNTAINS, THROUGH THE NIGHT LIT BRIGHT BY THE SHIMMERING NORTHERN LIGHTS.

THE KINGDOM OF ARENDELLE...

NIGHT BRINGS SLEEP FOR EVERYONE WITHN THE CASTLE WALLS...

...YOUNG AND OLD...

ELSA. PSST

ELSA. PSST
WAKE UP.

WAKE UP.
WAKE UP.
WAKE UP.

ANNA, GO BACK TO SLEEP.

I JUST CAN'T.

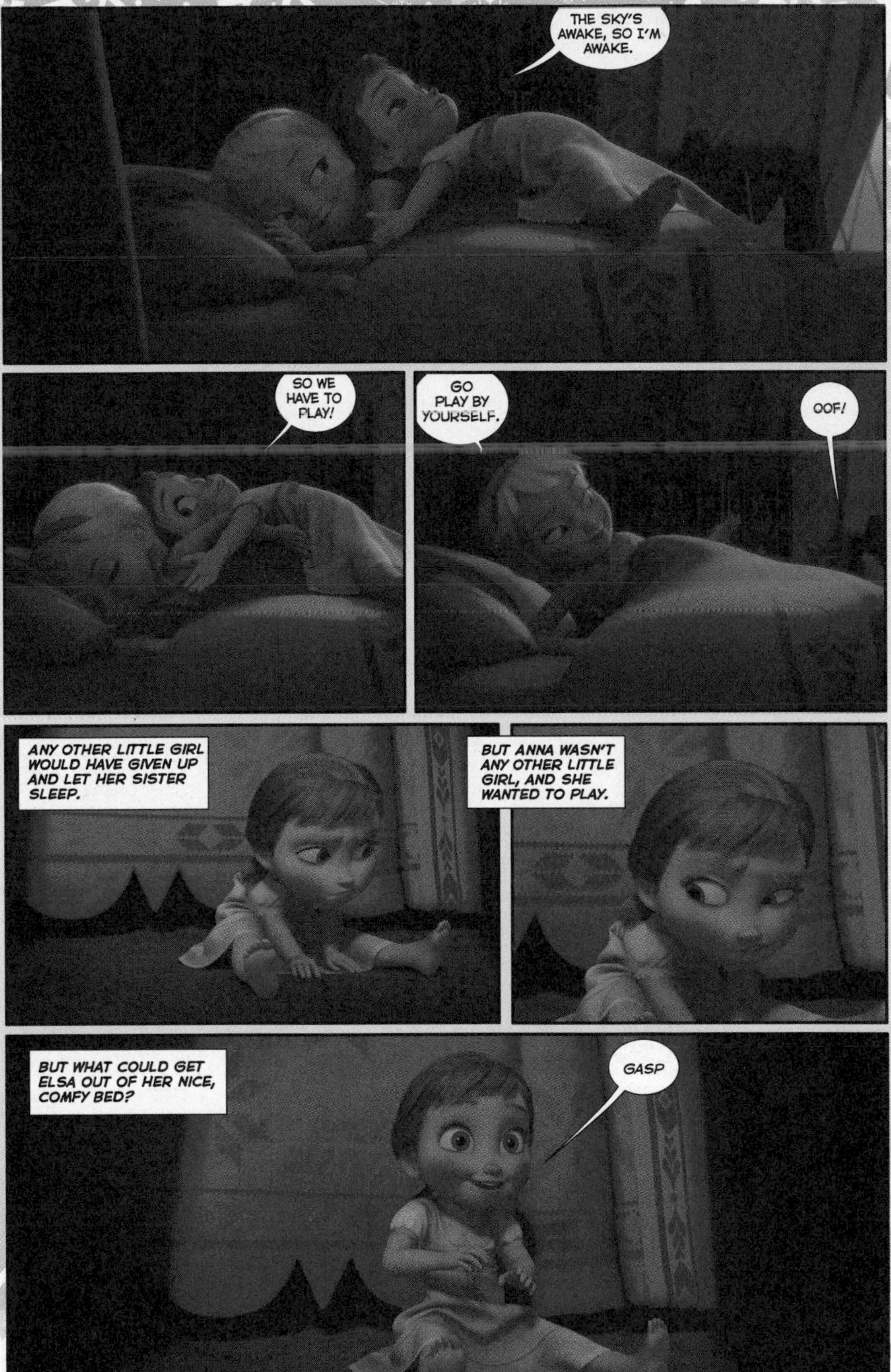

THE SKY'S AWAKE, SO I'M AWAKE.

SO WE HAVE TO PLAY!

GO PLAY BY YOURSELF.

OOF!

ANY OTHER LITTLE GIRL WOULD HAVE GIVEN UP AND LET HER SISTER SLEEP.

BUT ANNA WASN'T ANY OTHER LITTLE GIRL, AND SHE WANTED TO PLAY.

THERE WAS ONLY ONE THING.

ELSA...

...DO YOU WANT TO BUILD A SNOWMAN?

COME ON!
COME ON!
COME ON!

SHHH!
COME ON!

THE GIRLS RACE THROUGH THE CASTLE, GIGGLING AS QUIETLY AS THEY CAN...

...UNTIL THEY REACH THE GRAND BALLROOM, ONE OF THE BIGGEST ROOMS IN THE WHOLE CASTLE.

HEEHEE!
HAH!
AND THEY DID IT WITHOUT WAKING UP THEIR PARENTS!

DO THE MAGIC! DO THE MAGIC!

ELSA WAVES HER HANDS AND THINKS HARD...

...AND THE MAGIC COMES, GLITTERING IN THE DARK LIKE STARLIGHT.

OOH!

READY?

UH-HUH!

WHOOSH

ELSA'S MAGIC FLEW
TO THE HIGHEST POINT
IN THE GRAND HALL...

POP

...AND BECAME A
GENTLE SNOWFALL.

THIS IS
AMAZING!

WATCH THIS!

KR-TINK

CRAKCRAKCRAK

ICE!

HEEHEEHEE!

THE MAGIC SNOW CONTINUED TO FALL...

OOF!

AND SOON THERE WAS ENOUGH FOR THE GIRLS TO FINISH THEIR SNOWMAN.

"HI, I'M OLAF!"

"AND I LIKE WARM HUGS!"
OH!

I LOVE YOU, OLAF!

THE WORLD OUTSIDE THE PALACE DIDN'T EXIST THAT NIGHT FOR ANNA AND ELSA.
THAT NIGHT IT WAS JUST THE TWO OF THEM.
AND OLAF.

FOR ONE NIGHT ANNA AND ELSA WEREN'T PRINCESSES. THEY WEREN'T ROYALTY.

READY? ONE, TWO, THREE -- GO!

HA-HA!
TICKLE BUMPS!

TONIGHT, THEY WERE JUST TWO SISTERS, HAVING THE TIME OF THEIR LIVES.

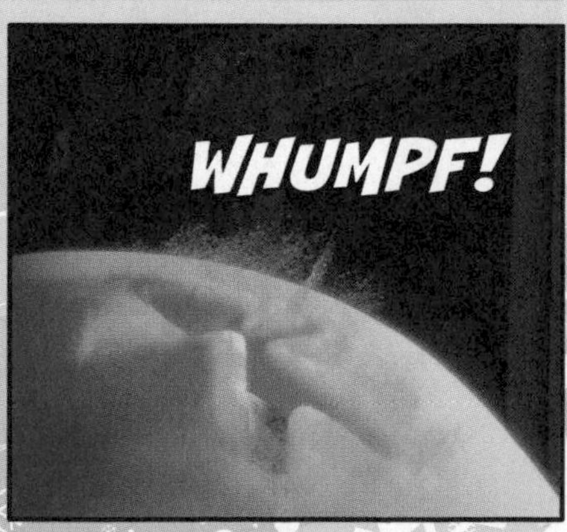
WHUMPF!

HAHAHAHA!
LET'S DO MORE!

HANG ON --

WHOO-HOO!

READY, ELSA?

CATCH ME!
GOTCHA!

HAHA! AGAIN!

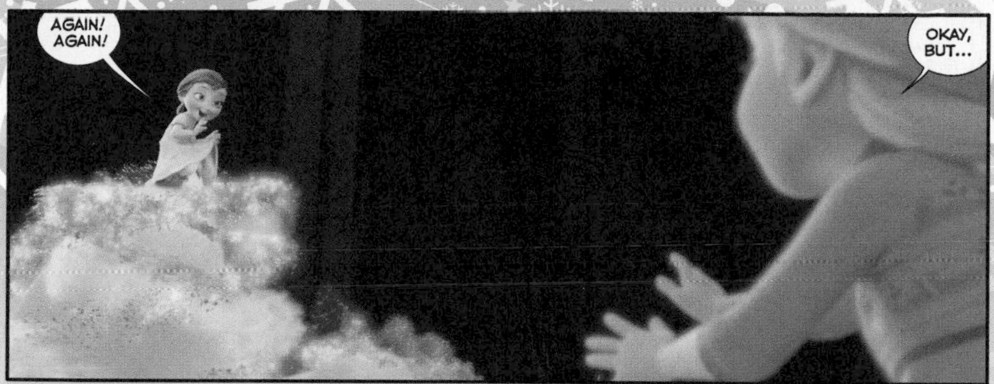
AGAIN! AGAIN!
OKAY, BUT...

JUST DON'T GO SO FAST!

WOO-HOO!

ANNA, SLOW DOWN!
WHOOPS --

WHOA!
STRUGGLING TO KEEP UP, ELSA SLIPS ...
...JUST AS ANNA JUMPED OFF THE HIGHEST SNOW PILE YET, STILL EXPECTING HER SISTER TO CATCH HER.

AFRAID HER SISTER WOULD FALL, ELSA REACHED OUT WITH HER MAGIC TOO QUICKLY, BEFORE SHE COULD FULLY REGAIN HER BALANCE...
ANNA!
FWASH

WHEE-HEE!

WHAM!
OWWW!

...WITH TRAGIC CONSEQUENCES.
UNNH...

Whump

GASP

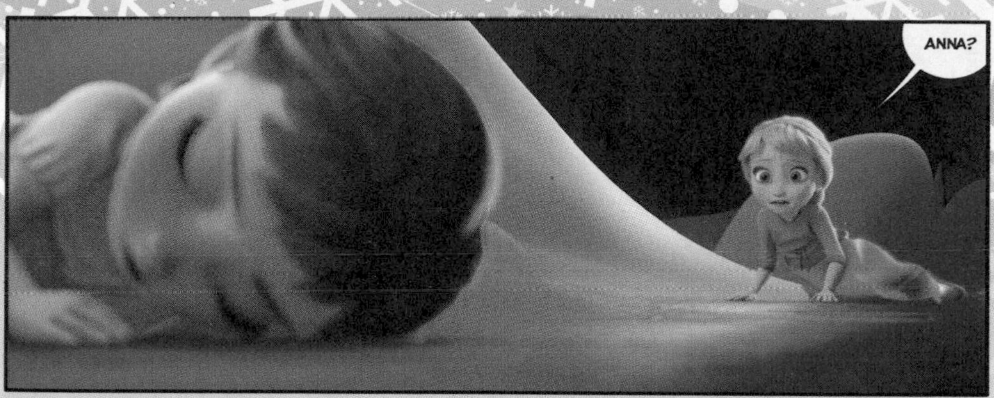
ANNA?

ELSA WAS SCARED -- ANNA HAD BEEN HIT WITH THE FULL FORCE OF HER ICE BLAST.
ANNA'S SKIN WAS ICE COLD.

ELSA WONDERED... COULD THIS BE HER FAULT?

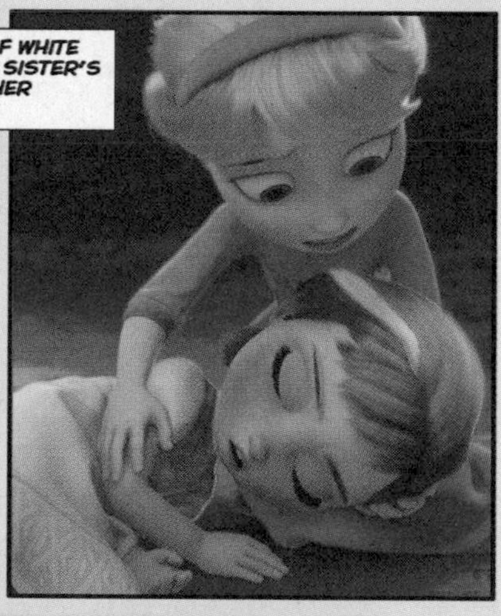
WHEN A STREAK OF WHITE APPEARED IN HER SISTER'S HAIR... SHE HAD HER ANSWER.

MAMA! PAPA!

NO, ANNA...

NO...

I DIDN'T MEAN IT. I DIDN'T MEAN IT.

PLEASE WAKE UP, ANNA. PLEASE

HER FOCUS BROKEN, ELSA'S CREATIONS FADE...

...LIKE MELTING FROST ON A WARM SUMMER'S MORNING.

IT'S OK, ANNA. I GOT YOU.

JUST THEN, THE KING AND QUEEN ARRIVE...
ELSA, WHAT HAVE YOU DONE? THIS IS GETTING OUT OF HAND.

ANNA!

IT WAS AN ACCIDENT.

SHE'S... SHE'S ICE COLD.

... I KNOW WHERE WE HAVE TO GO

THE KING RUSHES TO THE LIBRARY, SEARCHING FOR A BOOK HE HADN'T SEEN IN YEARS...
"THERE ARE LEGENDS, STORIES MY FATHER READ ME WHEN I WAS A BOY.

"I THOUGHT THEY WERE FAIRY TALES UNTIL HE TOOK ME DEEP INTO THE FOREST AND I SAW WITH MY OWN EYES..."
"SAW WHAT?"

"THERE IS A PLACE IN THE MOUNTAINS, WHERE MAGICAL BEINGS DWELL...

"...HEALERS THAT HAVE SERVED OUR KINGDOM IN TIMES OF NEED.

"WE CAN MAKE IT THERE TONIGHT ON HORSEBACK, WRAP ANNA TIGHT, KEEP HER WARM...

"...AND PRAY WE CAN FIND THEM."

"SHOULD WE TELL THE GUARDS?"

"NO...

"...WE TELL NO ONE."

IS THAT...

...ICE??

FASTER, SVEN!
HROOONK!

KRISTOFF AND SVEN FOLLOW THE ROYAL FAMILY -- AND THE STRANGE TRAIL OF ICE LEFT IN THEIR WAKE -- TO THE MOUNTAINS...

BRAA-AH!HH!
SHHH!

AND THEN... THE GROUND SHOOK, AS HUNDREDS OF STONES BEGAN TO MOVE.

RRRUMMBLE RRRUMMBBLE

RRRUMMBLE RRRUMMBBLE

RRRUMMBLE RRRUMMBBLE

WHOA.

THE BOULDERS SLOWED AS THEY NEARED THE ROYAL FAMILY.

AND THEN... THEY CAME TO LIFE.

IT'S THE KING.

...TROLLS?!

SHUSH!

I'M TRYING
TO LISTEN!

SLURP!

CUTIES. I'M
GONNA KEEP
YOU.

KRISTOFF, SVEN, AND THE TROLL LOOK ON AS THE ROYAL FAMILY IS GREETED BY GRAND PABBIE.
YOUR MAJESTY.

BORN WITH THE POWERS, OR CURSED?
BORN. AND THEY'RE GETTING STRONGER.

HERE. HERE.
HMM.

YOU ARE LUCKY IT WASN'T HER HEART.

THE HEART IS NOT SO EASILY CHANGED.
BUT THE HEAD CAN BE PERSUADED.
DO WHAT YOU MUST.

I RECOMMEND WE REMOVE ALL MAGIC, EVEN MEMORIES OF MAGIC, TO BE SAFE...

"BUT DON'T WORRY...

"...I'LL LEAVE THE FUN."

IT IS DONE.

SHE WILL BE OKAY.

BUT SHE WON'T REMEMBER I HAVE POWERS?
IT'S FOR THE BEST.
LISTEN TO ME CLOSELY, ELSA...

"THERE IS BEAUTY IN YOUR MAGIC..."

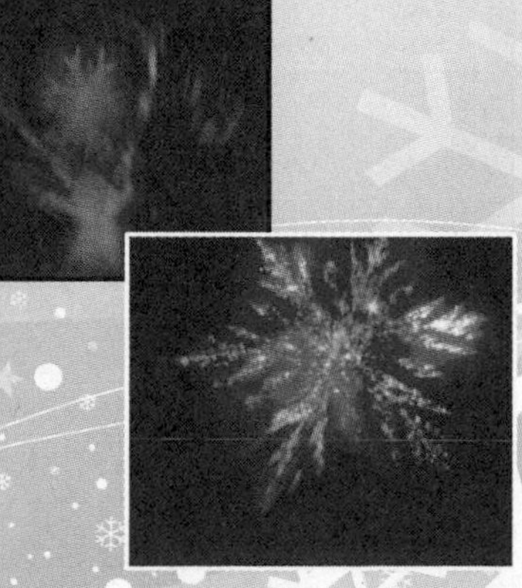

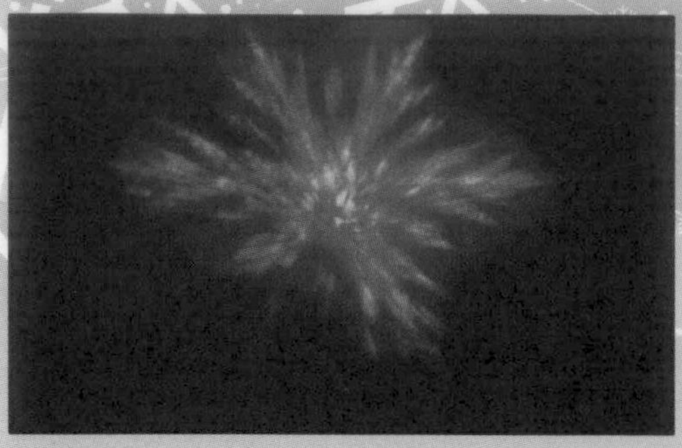

"-- BUT ALSO GREAT DANGER!

GASP!

"YOU MUST LEARN TO CONTROL IT."

"FEAR WILL BE YOUR ENEMY."
OH!

NO, WE'LL PROTECT HER.
SHE CAN LEARN TO CONTROL IT. I'M SURE.

"UNTIL THEN, WE'LL TAKE EVERY PRECAUTION."
"WE'LL LOCK THE GATES."
"WE'LL REDUCE THE STAFF."

"WE WILL LIMIT HER CONTACT WITH PEOPLE..."
...ELSA?
CLICK
"...INCLUDING ANNA."

AT THE NEXT SNOWFALL...

ELSA?
KNOCK KNOCK

ELSA -- PLEASE ANSWER ME.

WE COULD BUILD A SNOWMAN OUTSIDE.

YOU USED TO LOVE PLAYING IN THE SNOW.
IT WAS YOUR FAVORITE THING IN THE WHOLE WORLD.

NOW I NEVER SEE YOU.
PLEASE COME OUT.

IT'S ALMOST LIKE YOU'RE NOT THERE ANYMORE.
WE USED TO PLAY TOGETHER ALL THE TIME.
AND NOW YOU JUST IGNORE ME.
DID I DO SOMETHING WRONG?
COME ON -- WE DON'T HAVE TO BUILD A SNOWMAN.
WE CAN DO WHATEVER YOU WANT.
GO AWAY, ANNA.
...OKAY BYE.

I DO MISS YOU, ANNA.

I'D LIKE TO GO OUT AND PLAY...
...LIKE WE USED TO...

DON'T FRET, ELSA...

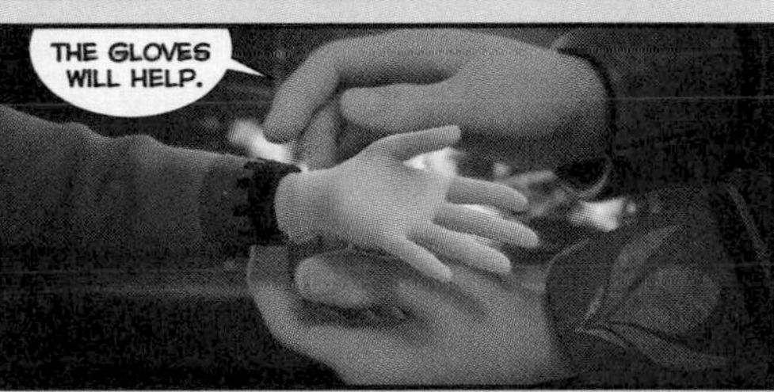
THE GLOVES WILL HELP.

SEE? YOU'RE GOOD. REMEMBER: CONCEAL IT.
DON'T FEEL IT.
DON'T LET IT SHOW.
AND SO THE KING AND QUEEN TRY TO HELP ELSA MASTER HER POWERS...

ELSA -- ARE YOU AWAKE?
KNOCK KNOCK
...AS YEARS PASS AND LIFE CONTINUES ON THE OTHER SIDE OF THE DOOR.

C'MON OUT, ELSA. I CAN HEAR YOU BREATHING.

EVERYONE'S OUTSIDE IN THE GARDEN. WE COULD RIDE OUR BIKES DOWN THE HALL!

WHEE!

UH-OH! LOOK OUT BELOW!

MAYBE WE CAN GO ON SOME ADVENTURES TOGETHER!

HANG IN THERE, JOAN.

GREAT -- NOW I'M TALKING TO THE PAINTINGS!

ELSA'S BEEN IN THERE SO LONG...

I WONDER WHAT SHE DOES IN THERE?

I'M SCARED. IT'S GETTING STRONGER.

GETTING UPSET ONLY MAKES IT WORSE.
DON'T TOUCH ME! I DON'T WANT TO HURT YOU.
CALM DOWN!

YOU COULD NEVER HURT US, ELSA. YOU HAVE TOO MUCH LOVE IN YOUR HEART.
WE'RE HERE WITH YOU, ELSA, EVERY DAY, FOR AS LONG AS IT TAKES.
THE DAYS TURN INTO WEEKS. THE WEEKS INTO MONTHS...

...AS ANNA GROWS FROM A LITTLE GIRL INTO A YOUNG WOMAN...

CAN'T I COME WITH YOU?

IT'S ONLY A SHORT TRIP, ANNA.

DO YOU HAVE TO GO?

YOU'LL BE FINE, ELSA.

ELSA?

"WE'LL ALWAYS HAVE EACH OTHER. I LOVE YOU."

I WISH I HAD MY SISTER BACK.

Three Years Later

SUMMER.
A TIME OF NEW BEGINNINGS AS THE KINGDOM PREPARES FOR A GRAND CELEBRATION...

WELCOME TO ARENDELLE!

WHY DO I HAVE TO WEAR THIS?

BECAUSE THE QUEEN HAS COME OF AGE.

-- IT'S CORONATION DAY!
...THAT'S NOT MY FAULT!

WHAT DO YOU WANT, SVEN?

give me a snack.

WHAT'S THE MAGIC WORD?

please!

CHOMP

UH! UH-UH-UH.

SHARE.

SHLURPP?

THAT'S BETTER.

I CAN'T BELIEVE THEY'RE FINALLY OPENING UP THE GATES, AGGIE!

AND FOR A WHOLE DAY, PERSI! HURRY, FASTER!

AH, ARENDELLE,
...OUR MOST MYSTERIOUS TRADE PARTNER!

OPEN THOSE GATES SO I MAY UNLOCK YOUR SECRETS AND EXPLOIT YOUR RICHES...

...DID I JUST SAY THAT OUT LOUD?

OH, ME SORE EYES CAN'T WAIT TO SEE THE QUEEN AND PRINCESS!

I BET THEY'RE ABSOLUTELY LOVELY!
I BET THEY ARE BEAUTIFUL!

ZZZZZZZ
KNOCK KNOCK
PRINCESS ANNA?

...HUH? YEAH?

SORRY TO WAKE YOU, MA'AM, BUT --
NO, YOU DIDN'T...

...I'VE BEEN UP...FOR HOURS... ZZZZZZZZ

SNORR-RR-R
KNOCK KNOCK
SNORT HM? WHA? WHO IS IT?

IT'S STILL ME, MA'AM. TIME TO GET READY.

READY FOR WHAT?

YOUR SISTER'S CORONATION, MA'AM.
THE CEREMONY STARTS SHORTLY.

CORONATION! IT'S CORONATION DAY! HA HA!

CORONATION DAY AND I ALMOST OVERSLEPT!

EVERYONE WILL BE HERE SOON, THE ENTIRE VILLAGE!

DAYLIGHT! REAL DAYLIGHT IN THE HALLS!

I NEVER THOUGHT I'D SEE THE PALACE SO ALIVE.

IT'S JUST LIKE I REMEMBER FROM WHEN I WAS LITTLE.

IT'LL BE LIKE THE OLD DAYS -- ONLY BIGGER!

THERE'LL BE GAMES AND LAUGHTER --

-- AND SINGING AND DANCING!

ELSA AND I WILL HAVE TO GREET EVERYONE.

WHAT SHOULD I SAY?

PAPA ALWAYS SAID SMILE AND SHAKE HANDS FIRMLY!
BETTER PRACTICE!

MAYBE A LITTLE LESS FIRM...!

IT'LL BE WONDERFUL TO HAVE SO MANY PEOPLE IN THE PALACE.

BUT I'LL BE READY!

I'VE DREAMT OF THIS FOR YEARS. THE MUSIC, THE BRIGHT LIGHTS.

IT SEEMS LIKE I'VE BEEN ASLEEP MY WHOLE LIFE ...

"... AND I'M FINALLY WAKING UP."

I CAN'T TELL IF I'M NERVOUS OR IT'S SOMETHING I ATE...

...BUT SOMETHING'S FLUTTERING IN MY STOMACH.

I GUESS I'VE JUST BEEN ALONE SO LONG...

I CAN'T WAIT TO MEET EVERYONE!

WHAT IF I MEET THE ONE?

THEN SOME HANDSOME STRANGER WILL ASK "WOULD I CARE TO DANCE?" OF COURSE!

WE'D DANCE AND EAT. OH, THE DESSERTS! SUCH RICH CHOCOLATES!

THE DASHING YOUNG PRINCE AND I WILL TALK THE NIGHT AWAY.

HE'LL LAUGH AT ALL MY JOKES.
I KNOW IT'S CRAZY TO DREAM OF ROMANCE, BUT ANYTHING COULD HAPPEN. ANYTHING!

ANYTHING COULD HAPPEN. ANYTHING.

ONE SLIP, ONE WRONG MOVE, AND I COULD HURT ALL THOSE PEOPLE.

I WANT TO BE THE DAUGHTER -- THE QUEEN -- YOU ALWAYS WANTED ME TO BE, PAPA.

I'M JUST SO WORRIED...

IF I LOSE CONTROL FOR EVEN A SECOND...

EVERYONE WILL SEE.

IT'S JUST ONE DAY.

TODAY'S THE DAY!

WHAT COULD GO WRONG?

DEEP BREATHS, ELSA. JUST FOR TODAY.

GUARDS! OPEN THE GATE!

YOU CAN DO THIS.

I CAN'T BELIEVE THIS IS REALLY HAPPENING!

JUST KEEP YOUR GLOVES ON AND REMEMBER WHAT PAPA SAID:
CONCEAL IT. DON'T FEEL IT.
DON'T LET IT SHOW.

THE GATES MAY CLOSE AGAIN TOMORROW.

SO I HAVE TO MAKE THE MOST OF TODAY.

SO MUCH TO SEE! SO MUCH TO DO!

I WANT TO SEE EVERYTHING!

AND NOTHING'S GOING TO STOP ME!

OOF!

WHOA-A-A- - !

MMMPH!
STOMP

I SHOULD --

I'M SO SORRY. ARE YOU HURT?

HEY. I-YA, NO. NO. I'M OKAY.

ARE YOU SURE?
YEAH, I JUST WASN'T LOOKING WHERE I WAS GOING. BUT I'M OKAY.

I'M GREAT, ACTUALLY.
OH, THANK GOODNESS.

WHOA, WHOA, WHOA, WHOA, WHOA!

OH!

HI...
AGAIN.

SNORT

UH-OH -- !
CREAK

OH BOY.

HA.
THIS IS
AWKWARD.
NOT YOU'RE
AWKWARD, BUT JUST
BECAUSE WE'RE--
I'M AWKWARD. YOU'RE
GORGEOUS.
WAIT --
WHAT?

I'D LIKE TO FORMALLY
APOLOGIZE FOR HITTING
THE PRINCESS OF
ARENDELLE WITH MY
HORSE...
...AND FOR
EVERY MOMENT
AFTER.
NO -- NO.
IT'S FINE.

I'M NOT THAT PRINCESS.

I MEAN, IF YOU'D HIT MY SISTER ELSA, THAT WOULD BE --

YEESH, Y'KNOW?

HELLO.

BUT, LUCKY YOU, IT'S-IT'S JUST ME.

JUST YOU?

HA
BONG BONG BONG

...THE BELLS. THE CORONATION.

I-I-I BETTER GO. I HAVE TO... I BETTER GO.
BYE!

WHINNEY
OH NO.

SPLASH!

HMPH!

BYE...

THE LAST TIME VOICES WERE RAISED IN SONG IN ARENDELLE'S GRAND CATHEDRAL IT WAS A TIME OF SORROW...
...TO MOURN THE PASSING OF THE KING AND QUEEN.

BUT TODAY THE CHURCH WALLS ECHO WITH SOUNDS OF JOY.

TODAY THE PEOPLE OF ARENDELLE AND VISITORS FROM ACROSS THE SEA GATHER IN CELEBRATION...
...AS A NEW QUEEN IS CROWNED.

A MONARCH TAKING THE THRONE IS A RARE EVENT.

SO ALL EYES ARE FOCUSED ON THE CEREMONY...

...ALMOST ALL.

IN SILENCE, THE CROWN IS PLACED ON ELSA'S HEAD.

NEXT, SHE'LL BE PRESENTED WITH THE ORB AND SCEPTER... AND THE CEREMONY WILL BE COMPLETE. SHE WILL BE QUEEN...

...AND EVERYTHING WILL GO BACK TO NORMAL.
AHEM...
YOUR MAJESTY... THE GLOVES...

ELSA HESITATED...

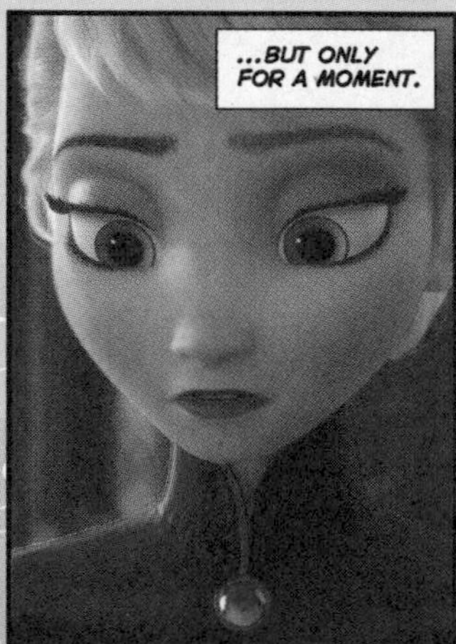
...BUT ONLY FOR A MOMENT.

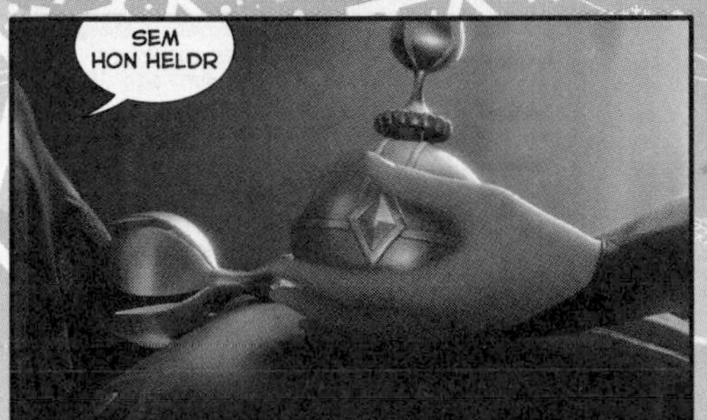
SEM
HON HELDR

INUM
HELGUM
EIGNUM

OK KRÝND Í ÞESSUM HELGA STAÐ EK TÉ FRAM FYRIR YÒR.
"AS SHE HOLDS THE TRADITIONAL RELICS AND IS CROWNED IN THIS PLACE, ALL RISE..."

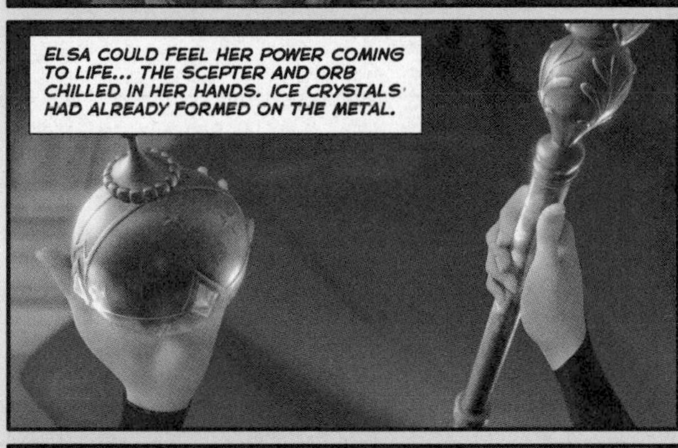
ELSA COULD FEEL HER POWER COMING TO LIFE... THE SCEPTER AND ORB CHILLED IN HER HANDS. ICE CRYSTALS HAD ALREADY FORMED ON THE METAL.

GASP!

...BUT THANKFULLY, ELSA SEEMED TO BE THE ONLY ONE WHO NOTICED.

THE NEW QUEEN RETURNED THE SYMBOLS OF HER REIGN TO THE BISHOP, AND PUT HER GLOVES BACK ON...
...BEFORE ANYONE WAS THE WISER.

QUEEN ELSA OF ARENDELLE!
...I PRESENT QUEEN ELSA OF ARENDELLE!
QUEEN ELSA OF ARENDELLE!

IT'S A JOY TO SEE THE PALACE ALIVE AGAIN.

YES -- THE GATES WERE CLOSED FAR TOO LONG.

HAS ANYONE SEEN THE QUEEN?
PRINCESS ANNA LOOKED SO LOVELY!
THE QUEEN LOOKS SO MUCH LIKE HER MOTHER!

I WONDER IF THE QUEEN WILL SPEAK TONIGHT?
I HOPE SO. WHAT A STORY TO TELL BACK HOME.

QUEEN ELSA OF ARENDELLE.

PRINCESS ANNA OF ARENDELLE.

OH!

AHEM.

HERE? ARE YOU SURE?
BECAUSE I DON'T THINK I'M SUPPOSED TO --

OH.
OKAY.

HAIL THE QUEEN AND PRINCESS!
CLAP CLAP CLAP
CLAP CLAP CLAP

...HI.

HI ME...? OH. UM. HI.
...YOU LOOK BEAUTIFUL.

THANK YOU. YOU LOOK BEAUTIFULLER. I MEAN, NOT FULLER.
YOU DON'T LOOK FULLER, BUT MORE BEAUTIFUL.
THANK YOU.

SO, THIS IS WHAT A PARTY LOOKS LIKE.
IT'S WARMER THAN I THOUGHT.

AND WHAT IS THAT AMAZING SMELL?
SNIFFFFFFFFF

...CHOCOLATE!

I--
YOUR MAJESTY.

THE DUKE OF WEASELTOWN!

WESELTON. THE DUKE OF WESELTON!

YOUR MAJESTY.
AS YOUR CLOSEST PARTNER IN TRADE, IT SEEMS ONLY FITTING--

--THAT I OFFER YOU YOUR FIRST DANCE AS QUEEN.

SHRRRIPPP

SNRRRT!
SHH!

THANK YOU... ONLY I DON'T DANCE.

OH...?
BUT MY SISTER DOES.
WHAT?

LUCKY YOU...
OH, I DON'T THINK...

IF YOU SWOON, LET ME KNOW, I'LL CATCH YOU!

SORRY.

I'M LIKE AN AGILE PEACOCK!
ER --
GOBBLE GOBBLE!

YAH-HAH!
SO GREAT TO HAVE THE GATES OPEN!

WHY DID THEY SHUT THEM IN THE FIRST PLACE?
OW!

DO YOU KNOW THE REASON?

HMMMM?
...NO.

NO.
ALL RIGHT. HANG ON!

THEY DON'T CALL ME THE LITTLE DIPPER FOR NOTHING!

SNORT GIGGLE

YOU DANCE DIVINELY, YOUR HIGHNESS!
GIGGLE

LIKE A CHICKEN... WITH THE FACE OF A MONKEY...

I FLY!

TWO SONGS LATER...
WELL, HE WAS SPRIGHTLY.
LET ME KNOW WHEN YOU'RE READY FOR ANOTHER ROUND, M'LADY.

ESPECIALLY FOR A MAN IN HEELS.
ARE YOU OKAY?

I'VE NEVER BEEN BETTER. THIS IS SO NICE.
I WISH IT COULD BE LIKE THIS ALL THE TIME.
ME TOO...

BUT IT CAN'T.

WHY NOT? I MEAN, WE--
IT JUST CAN'T.

EX-EXCUSE ME FOR A MINUTE.

SNIFF

--OH!
BUMP

!
WELL. GLAD I CAUGHT YOU.

PRINCE HANS!

ANNA SMILES, HAPPY TO SEE THE PRINCE AGAIN, AND EVEN HAPPIER TO DANCE WITH SOMEONE THAT DOESN'T HAVE THE FACE OF A MONKEY.

THEY DANCE...
...AND THEN THEY TALK.

...I OFTEN HAD THE WHOLE PARLOR TO MYSELF TO SLIDE AS FAST AS I COULD -- WHOOSH --

-- WHOOSH -- OOPS!
SMACK

MMFPF
HAHAHAHA

...YOUR PHYSIQUE HELPS, I'M SURE.

WHAT'S THAT STREAK?
I WAS BORN WITH IT...

...ALTHOUGH I DREAMT I WAS KISSED BY A TROLL.
I LIKE IT.

YEAH, EAT THE WHOLE THING! YOU GOT IT.
MMMPH. REMINDS ME OF MY FAVORITE SANDWICH.

SO YOU HAVE HOW MANY BROTHERS?

TWELVE OLDER BROTHERS. THREE OF THEM PRETENDED I WAS INVISIBLE... LITERALLY... FOR TWO YEARS.

THAT'S HORRIBLE
IT'S WHAT BROTHERS DO.
...AND SISTERS.

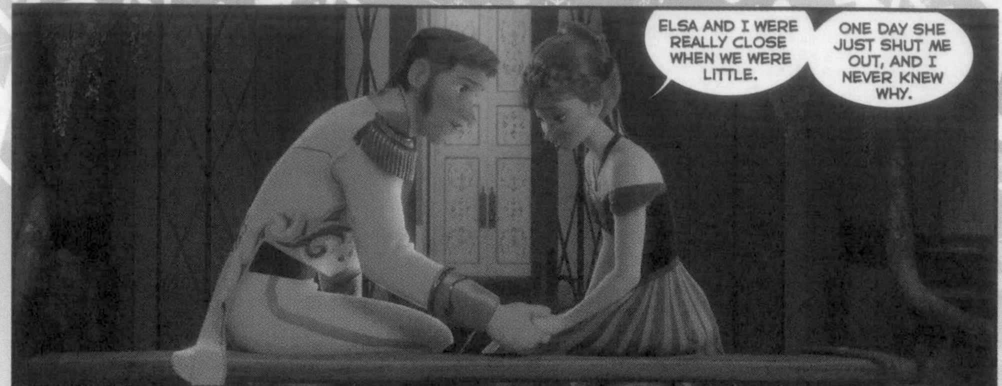
ELSA AND I WERE REALLY CLOSE WHEN WE WERE LITTLE.
ONE DAY SHE JUST SHUT ME OUT, AND I NEVER KNEW WHY.

I WOULD NEVER SHUT YOU OUT.
OKAY, CAN I JUST SAY SOMETHING CRAZY?
I LOVE CRAZY.

PEOPLE HAVE BEEN SHUTTING DOORS IN MY FACE MY WHOLE LIFE.

YOU'VE OPENED A DOOR TO ME.

THAT'S AMAZING! I WAS JUST GOING TO SAY...

...THAT I FELT THAT WAY TOO.

I'VE NEVER QUITE BELONGED. NEVER QUITE FIT IN.

THIS MIGHT BE THE PARTY TALKING...

...OR MAYBE I OVERDID IT ON THE FONDUE...

BUT I FEEL I BELONG HERE. WITH YOU.

I LOOK INTO YOUR EYES...

AND I LOSE MYSELF.

I WANT TO OPEN THE DOOR!

I WANT TO OPEN THE DOOR!

WE'LL OPEN IT TOGETHER!

SHH! WE HAVE TO BE QUIET!

YOU FIRST!
NO, YOU FIRST!

ANYONE THERE?

BWA-HA-HAHAHA!

IT'S HARD TO BELIEVE
WHAT IS?
HOW WE ALWAYS SEEM TO KNOW --

--WHAT THE OTHER PERSON IS GOING TO SAY?
EXACTLY!

I'VE NEVER KNOWN ANYONE

WHO GETS ME THE WAY YOU DO.

JINX! DOUBLE JINX!

HOW DO YOU EXPLAIN THIS PERFECT HARMONY?

YOU--
-- WE --
-- ME --
-- IT'S --

OUR DESTINY.
OUR DESTINY.

FAREWELL--
FAREWELL--

WE'RE GOING FORWARD TOGETHER--
--TO THE LIFE THAT WE ONCE KNEW!

--TWO BY TWO!

CAN THIS BE REAL, ANNA? IS THIS A DREAM?

IF IT'S A DREAM I DON'T EVER WANT TO WAKE UP.

MY LIFE
IS SO MUCH
BETTER --

SINCE...

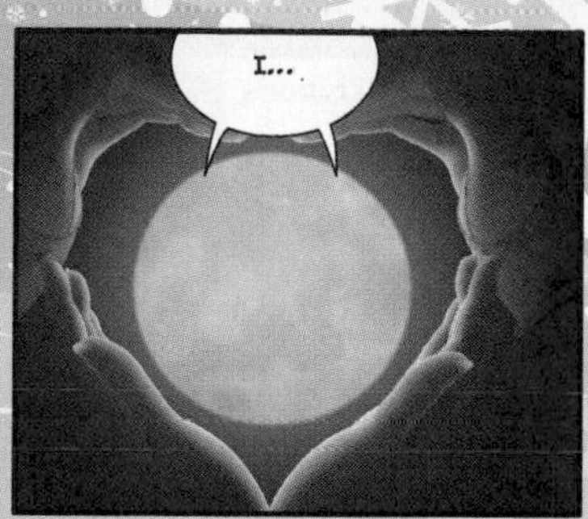
I...

MET YOU!

CAN I SAY
SOMETHING
CRAZY...?
WILL YOU
MARRY ME?

CAN I
JUST SAY
SOMETHING
EVEN
CRAZIER?
YES.

"EXCUSE ME! PARDON ME! IN A HURRY!

OOPS! PARDON. SORRY. CAN WE JUST GET AROUND YOU THERE?

THANK YOU. OH, THERE SHE IS. ELSA!

I MEAN... QUEEN... ME AGAIN.

UM. MAY I PRESENT PRINCE HANS OF THE SOUTHERN ISLES.
YOUR MAJESTY.

WE WOULD LIKE --
--YOUR BLESSING --
--OF --

-- OUR MARRIAGE!

MARRIAGE...?

YES!
I'M SORRY-- I'M CONFUSED
WELL, WE HAVEN'T WORKED OUT ALL THE DETAILS OURSELVES. WE'LL NEED A FEW DAYS TO PLAN THE CEREMONY.

OF COURSE, WE'LL HAVE SOUP, ROAST, AND ICE CREAM AND THEN -- WAIT. WOULD WE LIVE HERE?

HERE?

ABSOLUTELY!
ANNA--

OH, WE CAN INVITE ALL TWELVE OF YOUR BROTHERS TO STAY WITH US --
WHAT? NO, NO, NO, NO, NO.

I DON'T KNOW. SOME OF THEM MUST --
WAIT. SLOW DOWN. NO ONE'S BROTHERS ARE STAYING HERE.

NO ONE IS GETTING MARRIED.

WAIT, WHAT?
MAY I TALK TO YOU, ANNA, PLEASE. ALONE.

NO. WHATEVER YOU HAVE TO SAY, YOU-YOU CAN SAY TO BOTH OF US.

FINE. YOU CAN'T MARRY A MAN YOU JUST MET.

YOU CAN IF IT'S TRUE LOVE.

ANNA, WHAT DO YOU KNOW ABOUT TRUE LOVE?
MORE THAN YOU.

YOU ASKED FOR MY BLESSING, BUT MY ANSWER IS NO.

THE PARTY IS OVER. CLOSE THE GATES.

WHAT?

ELSA, NO. WAIT!
LET GO OF MY GLOVE!

ELSA, PLEASE. PLEASE. I CAN'T LIVE LIKE THIS ANYMORE.

...THEN LEAVE.

...WHAT DID I EVER DO TO YOU?!

ENOUGH, ANNA

ELSA TURNED TO LEAVE, AFRAID HER POWERS MIGHT SUDDENLY RUN OUT OF CONTROL.
BUT ANNA WASN'T DONE WITH HER YET.
NO, WHY?

WHY DO YOU SHUT ME OUT?

WHY DO YOU SHUT THE WORLD OUT?

WHAT ARE YOU SO AFRAID OF?

I SAID
ENOUGH!

CRACKLLLLL

MY
WORD...!
WHAT IS
THAT?
IS THAT
ICE?
?!

IT CAME
FROM HER
HANDS!
WHAT IS
SHE?

...

...SORCERY. I KNEW THERE WAS SOMETHING DUBIOUS GOING ON HERE.

ELSA...?

HER POWER WAS FINALLY REVEALED. IT WAS ELSA'S GREATEST FEAR COME TO LIFE.

SHE DIDN'T KNOW WHAT TO SAY OR DO...

...SO SHE RAN.
OH, ELSA.

GASP
THERE SHE IS!

CLAPCLAPCLAPCLAP
CLAPCLAPCLAP

YES, IT IS HER!

QUEEN ELSA!

YOUR HIGHNESS--!

YOUR MAJESTY?
ARE YOU ALL
RIGHT?

...NO...
ELSA BACKED AWAY FROM THE CONCERNED WOMAN. SHE STILL HOPED TO ESCAPE BEFORE ANYONE ELSE SAW HER POWER.

KRRRRIKK
BUT SHE BACKED INTO THE FOUNTAIN, WHERE HER BARE HAND TOUCHED THE WET STONE...

...AND FROZE THE FOUNTAIN'S SPOUT INTO SOLID ICE IN FRONT OF EVERYONE.
KRRAAKKAAKAKK

GASP!
THE FOUNTAIN --
IS IT MAGIC?

THERE SHE IS! STOP HER!

PLEASE, JUST STAY AWAY FROM ME. STAY AWAY!

CRRKKKLLLL

WATCH OUT!
OOF!
AGH!
WATCH OUT!

MONSTER.... MONSTER!

THE PEOPLE HEARD THE DUKE, AND MOVED BACK.

ELSA SAW FEAR IN THEIR EYES.

THE PEOPLE WHO HAD CHEERED HER JUST MOMENTS AGO WERE SHRINKING AWAY.

MAYBE THE DUKE WAS RIGHT. MAYBE SHE WAS A MONSTER... BUT SHE COULDN'T BEAR THE THOUGHT OF HURTING ANYONE...
SO SHE RAN.

ELSA!

ELSA, WAIT! PLEASE!

ELSA HEARD HER SISTER, AND RAN EVEN FASTER. OUT OF THE CASTLE, ELSA RAN...

...OUT OF ARENDELLE...

GASP

...STOPPING WHEN SHE REACHED THE FJORD.

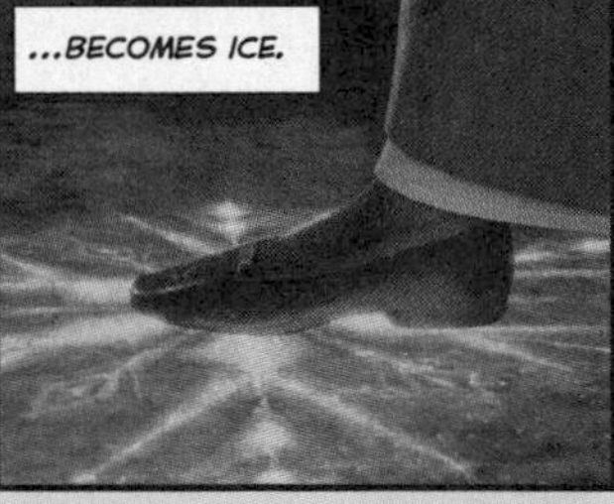

AS SHE HAD WITH THE FOUNTAIN, ELSA FROZE OVER THE FJORD WITH HER POWER AND KEPT ON, LEAVING ARENDELLE - AND ANNA - BEHIND.

ELSA, COME BACK!
ANNA!

NO.

ELSA! ELSA!!

ANNA... LOOK....

"... THE FJORD."

"IT'S FREEZING OVER."
KRRAAAKAKAK

KRRRAAAAKKK

KRAAAKAKKAKKK

...SNOW?
IT'S... SNOW...IN JULY.

...ARE YOU ALL RIGHT?
...NO...

LOOK! IT'S SNOWING! IT'S SNOWING!
THE QUEEN HAS CURSED THIS LAND! SHE MUST BE STOPPED!

YOU HAVE TO GO AFTER HER!
SHE'S A MONSTER!
WAIT -- NO!

YOU! IS THERE SORCERY IN YOU, TOO?
NO. NO. I'M COMPLETELY ORDINARY.

THAT'S RIGHT SHE IS...
...IN THE BEST WAY.
...AND MY SISTER'S NOT A MONSTER.

SHE NEARLY KILLED ME.
YOU SLIPPED ON ICE.
HER ICE!
IT WAS AN ACCIDENT. SHE WAS SCARED. SHE DIDN'T MEAN ANY OF THIS....

TONIGHT WAS MY FAULT. I PUSHED HER. SO I'M THE ONE THAT NEEDS TO GO AFTER HER.
YES. FINE. DO.

WHAT?
KAI, BRING ME MY HORSE, PLEASE.

ANNA, NO. IT'S TOO DANGEROUS.

ELSA'S NOT DANGEROUS. I'LL BRING HER BACK, AND I'LL MAKE THIS RIGHT.

I'M COMING WITH YOU.
NO, I NEED YOU HERE TO TAKE CARE OF ARENDELLE.
I LEAVE PRINCE HANS IN CHARGE!
...ON MY HONOR.

ARE YOU SURE YOU CAN TRUST HER? I DON'T WANT YOU GETTING HURT.

SHE'S MY SISTER --

--SHE WOULD NEVER HURT ME.
HYAH!

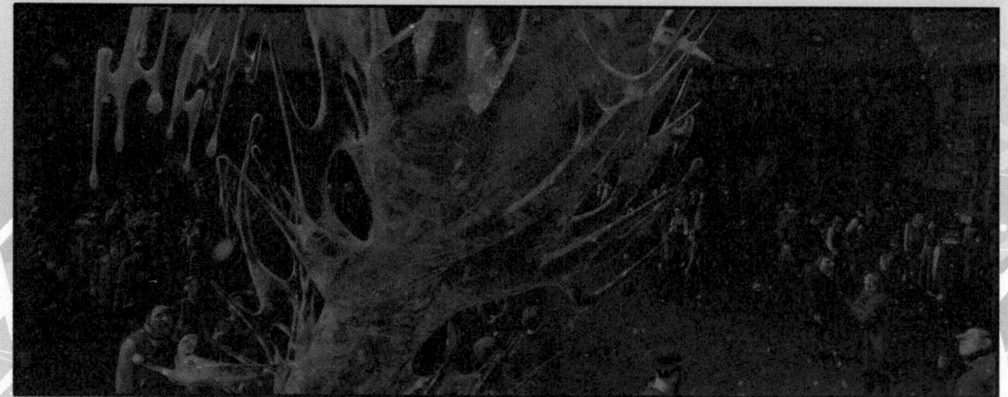

AS THE MAGICAL BLIZZARD RAGES IN THE MOUNTAINS...
...ELSA RUNS FROM HER PAST, TOWARD AN UNCERTAIN FUTURE...
I NEVER MEANT FOR THIS TO HAPPEN.
EVERYONE THINKS I'M SOME KIND OF MONSTER.
THE QUEEN OF SNOW AND ICE AND COLD.
I TRIED SO HARD.
I TRIED TO KEEP IT IN.

THEY TOLD ME NOT TO LET THEM SEE.

THEY TOLD ME TO HIDE WHAT I WAS...

...WHAT I COULD DO.

BUT THERE'S NO MORE HIDING NOW.

I CAN FINALLY BE...

...FREE.

WHOOOSH!

NO MORE HOLDING BACK.

SO LET'S SEE WHAT I CAN REALLY DO!

THE WIND AND THE ICE AND THE SNOW --

--ARE MINE TO COMMAND.

FOR THE FIRST TIME IN MY LIFE...

...I'M FINALLY FREE!

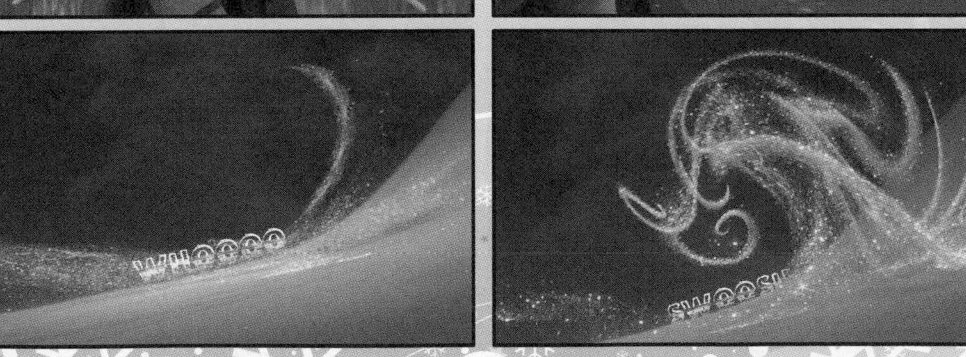

IT DOESN'T MATTER WHAT OTHER PEOPLE THINK

NOT ANYMORE.

SO LET THE WIND BLOW AND THE SNOW FALL!

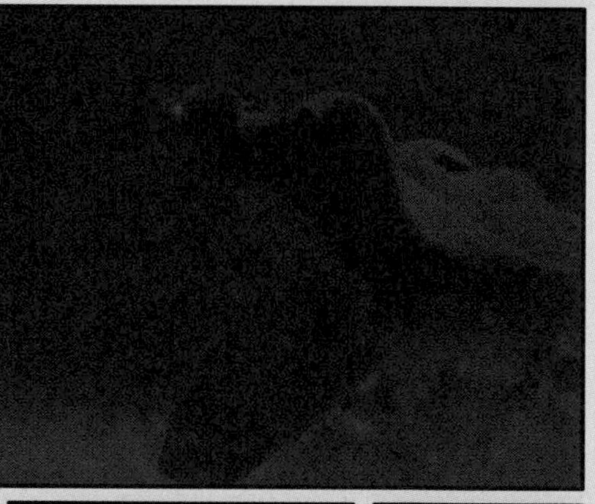

BESIDES, I'VE ALWAYS LIKED THE COLD.

FROM WAY UP HERE...

...EVERYTHING LOOKS SO... DIFFERENT.

IT'S LIKE I'M SEEING CLEARLY FOR THE FIRST TIME.

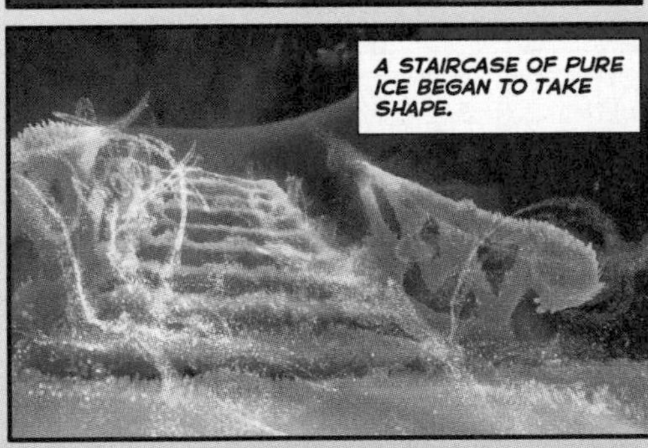
A STAIRCASE OF PURE ICE BEGAN TO TAKE SHAPE.

ONE THAT WOULD TAKE HER EVER HIGHER INTO THE MOUNTAINS.

THIS IS INCREDIBLE!

WHY WAS I HOLDING BACK ALL THOSE YEARS?

NEVER, EVER

NEVER, EVER AGAIN!

ICE CRYSTALS SHIMMER AS THEY SWIRL AND DANCE IN THE MOONLIGHT.

ELSA'S POWER SENDS COLUMNS OF ICE SOARING UP FROM THE GROUND...

...UNTIL AROUND HER STANDS A GLORIOUS ICE PALACE.

THIS IS MY HOME NOW.

AND HERE...

...I CAN FINALLY BE MYSELF.

THE OLD ME...

...IS GONE.

NO MORE HIDING IN THE SHADOWS.

I'M GOING TO STAND IN THE LIGHT!

I TRIED TO BE WHAT THEY WANTED ME TO BE.

BUT NO MORE!

DO YOU
HEAR ME
WORLD?

I'M NOT
GOING TO BE
YOUR PERFECT
PRINCESS
ANYMORE!

I'M
GOING
TO BE...

...ME.

SLAM!

MEANWHILE, IN A VALLEY FAR FROM THE MOUNTAIN...
ELSA! ELSA! IT'S ME, ANNA... YOUR SISTER WHO DIDN'T MEAN TO MAKE YOU FREEZE THE SUMMER.

I'M SORRY. IT'S ALL MY F-F-F-F-F -F-FAULT.
OF COURSE, NONE OF THIS WOULD HAVE HAPPENED IF SHE'D JUST TOLD ME HER SECRET
HOWLLL

HA...SHE'S A STINKER.
DON'T WORRY -- THAT WOLF IS PROBABLY FAR AWAY...
HOWLLL

YOW!
SWACK

WHINNEY!

OOF!

PTUI.

OH, NO --
WHINNEY!

--NO, NO, NO!
COME BACK!

NO. NO. NO. NO.... OOOO-KAY.

NO PROBLEM. I CAN HANDLE THIS --JUST PULL MYSELF OUT AND --

MMMPH!
WHUMPF!

PERFECT. JUST PERFECT.

SNOW, IT HAD TO BE SNOW, SHE COULDN'T HAVE HAD TR-TR-TROPICAL MAGIC...

AND COVER THE F-F-FJORDS WITH WHITE SANDS AND WARM --

FIRE!
ANNA HAS SPOTTED SMOKE IN THE DISTANCE. BUT AS SHE MOVES TOWARD IT...

...SHE SLIPS ON SOME ICE...
WHUP-WHUP-WHOA!

...ROLLS DOWN A HILL...
AAAAAAHHHHH--

...AND LANDS RIGHT IN A CHILLY STREAM.
ACK!
Kr-splash

COLD, COLD, COLD, COLD, COLD...

BUT AT LEAST IT GOT HER CLOSER TO THE FIRE.
...COLD, COLD, COLD, COLD, COLD...

...COLD, COLD -- LOOKS LIKE SOMEONE'S HOME. BUT WHO WOULD BE LIVING ALL ALONE OUT HERE?

MAYBE IF I BRUSH OFF SOME OF THIS SNOW...

TRADING POST --

WANDERING OAKEN'S
TRADING POST
-- OOH! AND SAUNA!
BRRR...
HELLO -- IS ANYONE --
WHOOOSH!
EEP!
SLAM!
HOO HOO!
HMM?
BIG SUMMER BLOWOUT!
HALF OFF SWIMMING SUITS, CLOGS --
-- AND A SUNBALM OF MY OWN INVENTION, YAH?

OH -- GREAT. FOR NOW, HOW ABOUT WINTER BOOTS...AND DRESSES?
THAT WOULD BE IN OUR WINTER DEPARTMENT.

...OH.

UM... I WAS JUST WONDERING -- HAS ANOTHER YOUNG WOMAN, THE QUEEN PERHAPS, I DON'T KNOW, PASSED THROUGH HERE?

ONLY ONE CRAZY ENOUGH TO BE OUT IN THIS STORM IS YOU, DEAR.

WHOOOSH!

ARE YOU OPEN FOR BUSINESS?

YOU AND THIS FELLOW....

UHH...
HOO HOO. BIG SUMMER BLOW OUT!

CARROTS.
...HUH...?

BEHIND YOU.

OH, RIGHT. EXCUSE ME.

A REAL HOWLER IN JULY, YAH?
PLOP!
WHERE EVER COULD IT BE COMING FROM?
THE NORTH MOUNTAIN.
NORTH MOUNTAIN.
WHAT DO I OWE YOU?
THAT'LL BE FORTY.
FORTY? NO, TEN.
OH DEAR, THAT'S NO GOOD. SEE THESE ARE FROM OUR WINTER STOCK, WHERE SUPPLY AND DEMAND HAVE A BIG PROBLEM.
YOU WANT TO TALK ABOUT A SUPPLY AND DEMAND PROBLEM?
I SELL ICE FOR A LIVING.

OOH, THAT'S A ROUGH BUSINESS TO BE IN RIGHT NOW. I MEAN, THAT IS REALLY...
AHEM. THAT'S UNFORTUNATE.

STILL FORTY. BUT I WILL THROW IN A VISIT TO OAKEN'S SAUNA. HOO HOO! HI, FAMILY.

HOO HOO!

TEN'S ALL I GOT.

HELP ME OUT.
OKAY.

TEN WILL GET YOU THIS AND NO MORE.

OKAY, JUST TELL ME ONE THING -- WHAT WAS HAPPENING ON THE NORTH MOUNTAIN?

DID IT SEEM MAGICAL?

YES.
NOW BACK OFF--

--WHILE I DEAL WITH THIS CROOK, HERE...
GULP

WHAT DID YOU CALL ME?

OKAY. OKAY, I'M-OW!

BYE BYE.
WHOA!

FOR THE FIRST TIME SINCE THE FREAK STORM STARTED, KRISTOFF FOUND HIMSELF HAPPY FOR THE SNOW--
WHUMPF!

--IF NOTHING ELSE, IT MADE FOR A SOFT LANDING.
SNORT!

SNIFF SNIFF
SNRRRT?

NO, SVEN, I DIDN'T GET YOUR CARROTS.

BUT I DID FIND US A PLACE TO SLEEP. A COZY WARM BARN. AND IT'S FREE!

I'M SORRY ABOUT THIS VIOLENCE.
I WILL ADD A QUART OF LUTEFISK SO WE HAVE GOOD FEELINGS.

SO... JUST THE OUTFIT AND THE BOOTS, YAH?

AHHH... HMM.

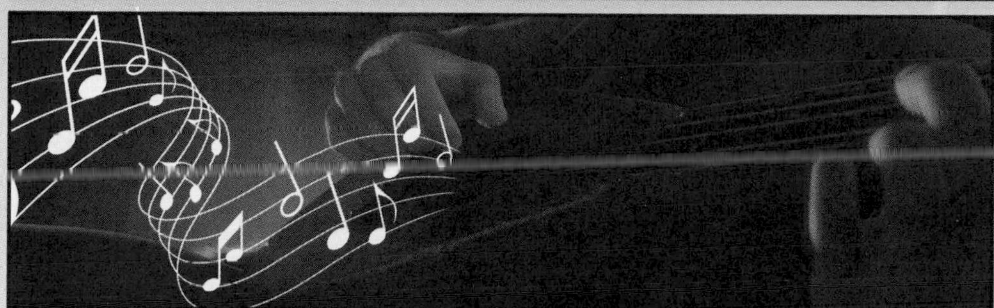

It's true. people are cruel and loud, and they'll lie to your face. They're terrible, all except you.

AWWW...
THANKS,
PAL.
YOU ALWAYS KNOW JUST WHAT TO SAY.
BUT IN DEFENSE OF PEOPLE, WE DO SMELL BETTER THAN REINDEER.

SVEN, WOULDN'T YOU AGREE?

I would have to agree...

...except for you.
OOOH, GOOD ONE. NOW HOW ABOUT WE HIT THE LITERAL HAY?
sounds okay to me. good night, kristoff.
GOOD NIGHT, SVEN.

NICE DUET.
YAAAGH!
HAWW!
OH, IT'S JUST YOU. WHAT DO YOU WANT?
I WANT YOU TO TAKE ME UP THE NORTH MOUNTAIN.
I DON'T TAKE PEOPLE PLACES.

ANNA TOSSES KRISTOFF A BAG OF SUPPLIES AND SAYS:
LET ME REPHRASE THAT--

TAKE ME UP THE NORTH MOUNTAIN ... PLEASE.

SNFF SNFF

WHY DO YOU WANT TO GO UP THE MOUNTAIN?

I KNOW HOW TO STOP THIS WINTER.

OK, WE LEAVE AT DAWN.... AND YOU FORGOT THE CARROTS FOR SVEN.

UGH!
WHACK!

OOPS! SORRY! SORRY!
WHAT THE -- ?

I'M SORRY. I DIDN'T --

-- I MEAN, WE LEAVE NOW. RIGHT NOW.

WHEW.
CHOMP.
...?
FOUR AND A HALF CARROTS LATER...
THEY'RE ON THEIR WAY.

HANG ON -
WE LIKE TO
GO FAST!

THAT'S
OK -- I LIKE
FAST!

WHOA, WHOA!
GET YOUR
FEET DOWN.

THIS IS
FRESH LACQUER.
SERIOUSLY, WERE
YOU RAISED IN
A BARN?
SPI--
TOO!
EW! NO,
I WAS RAISED
IN A CASTLE.

SO TELL
ME, WHAT MADE
THE QUEEN GO
ALL ICE-
CRAZY?

...OH WELL, IT WAS ALL MY FAULT.
I GOT ENGAGED BUT THEN SHE FREAKED OUT BECAUSE I'D ONLY JUST MET HIM--
-- YOU KNOW, THAT DAY. AND SHE SAID SHE WOULDN'T BLESS THE MARRIAGE--

WAIT. YOU GOT ENGAGED TO SOMEONE YOU JUST MET?

YEAH. ANYWAY, I GOT MAD AND SO SHE GOT MAD AND THEN SHE TRIED TO WALK AWAY, AND I GRABBED HER GLOVE--

HANG ON. YOU MEAN TO TELL ME YOU GOT ENGAGED TO SOMEONE YOU JUST MET?!
YES. PAY ATTENTION.

BUT THE THING IS SHE WORE THE GLOVES ALL THE TIME...

...SO I JUST THOUGHT, MAYBE SHE HAS A THING ABOUT DIRT.

DIDN'T YOUR PARENTS EVER WARN YOU ABOUT STRANGERS?

YES, THEY DID.... BUT HANS IS NOT A STRANGER.

OH YEAH? WHAT'S HIS LAST NAME?
...OF-THE-SOUTHERN-ISLES?

WHAT'S HIS FAVORITE FOOD?
...SANDWICHES.

BEST FRIEND'S NAME?
PROBABLY JOHN.
EYE COLOR?
DREAMY.

FOOT SIZE...?
FOOT SIZE DOESN'T MATTER.

HAVE YOU HAD A MEAL WITH HIM YET? WHAT IF YOU HATE THE

WHAT IF YOU HATE THE WAY HE PICKS HIS NOSE?
PICKS HIS NOSE?
AND EATS IT.
EXCUSE ME, SIR. HE'S A PRINCE.

ALL MEN DO IT.
EW. LOOK, IT DOESN'T MATTER; IT'S TRUE LOVE.

DOESN'T SOUND LIKE TRUE LOVE.
ARE YOU SOME SORT OF LOVE EXPERT?
NO. BUT I HAVE FRIENDS WHO ARE.

WHOA, SVEN, WHOA.
YOU HAVE FRIENDS WHO ARE LOVE EXPERTS.... I'M NOT BUYING IT.
NO, NO, NO. I'D LIKE TO MEET THESE--
STOP TALKING.

MMMPH!
I MEAN IT. SHHH.

HEY!

SHH!

SNRRT?

AT FIRST, ANNA THOUGHT KRISTOFF WAS TRYING TO MAKE A FOOL OF HER...
...TRYING TO GET BACK AT HER FOR TEASING HIM ABOUT THE LOVE EXPERTS.

BUT THEN,
SHE HEARS IT.

GRRRRRRRRRRRRRRRRRRR

SVEN -
GO.
GO!

WHAT
ARE
THEY?
WOLVES...

WOLVES?!

WOLVES. WHAT DO WE DO?
I'VE GOT THIS. YOU JUST...DON'T FALL OFF AND DON'T GET EATEN.
BUT I WANNA HELP.
NO.
WHY NOT?
BECAUSE I DON'T TRUST YOUR JUDGMENT.
EXCUSE ME?!
WHO MARRIES A MAN SHE JUST MET?!
IT'S TRUE LOVE!
WHOA!
WHUNG
JUST IN TIME, ANNA STOPS THE WOLF FROM ATTACKING KRISTOFF.

WHOA!!
SNARL
SNAP

CHRISTOPHER!
YAAAGH!

OOF! OUCH! AGH!

IT'S KRISTOFF! AGH!

ANNA LOOKS FOR A WAY TO HELP KRISTOFF... AND FINDS ONE.

USING HER TORCH, SHE LIGHTS HIS BEDROLL ON FIRE...

KRISTOFF! GET READY!
??!
DUCK!
WHOA!!
WHAM!
ARGH!
YELPH!
ANNA --
GRRR!
SNARRLL!
YOU ALMOST SET ME ON FIRE!

KRISTOFF PULLS HIMSELF BACK ONTO THE SLED JUST IN TIME --

SNRRRT??!

-- BECAUSE THINGS ARE ABOUT TO GET MUCH, MUCH WORSE."

OH!
GET READY TO JUMP, SVEN!
YOU DON'T TELL HIM WHAT TO DO - I DO!

ANNA WAS ABOUT TO PROTEST WHEN KRISTOFF SCOOPED HER UP AND TOSSED HER ONTO SVEN'S BACK...

--OOF!

OKAY, NOW--
SVISH
...AND THEN CUT THE ROPES THAT HELD SVEN TO THE SLED.

JUMP, SVEN!

JUMP!

AAAAGGHHH!!!

AAAAAGGGHHH!!!
AWRRHR!

SVEN CLEARS THE GORGE WITHOUT ANY TROUBLE --

OOOF!
--BUT THE SLED DOESN'T HAVE ENOUGH SPEED TO CROSS THE GAP.

KRISTOFF JUMPS AT THE LAST SECOND...

YES!

GRRRRR
GRRRRR
GRRRRR

WHEW.
HANGING ON THE EDGE, KRISTOFF TAKES A QUICK LOOK BELOW FOR HIS SLED.

MAYBE THE SNOW BROKE ITS FALL?

WHOOM!
AW -- BUT I JUST PAID IT OFF --!

UH-OH. NO, NO, NO

SWOOSH!
HANG ON!

?!
THUNK!
GRAB ON!

PULL, SVEN! PULL!

SLOWLY, SVEN PULLS KRISTOFF UP FROM THE EDGE.

WITH ANNA'S HELP, OF COURSE.

WHEW.
THAT WAS TOO CLOSE.

I'M SO SORRY... I'LL REPLACE YOUR SLED AND EVERYTHING IN IT...
AND I UNDERSTAND IF YOU DON'T WANT TO HELP ME ANYMORE.

AS ANNA SETS OFF ON HER OWN, KRISTOFF AND SVEN WEIGH THEIR OPTIONS.
SNRRT?

OF COURSE I DON'T WANT TO HELP HER ANYMORE. IN FACT, THIS WHOLE THING HAS RUINED ME FOR HELPING ANYONE EVER AGAIN.

but she'll die on her own.
I CAN LIVE WITH THAT.
but you won't get your new sled if she's dead.

...YOU KNOW SOMETIMES I REALLY DON'T LIKE YOU.
SIGH HOLD UP! WE'RE COMING!

YOU ARE?!
I MEAN -- SURE, I'LL LET YOU TAG ALONG.
...

LATER... ANNA AND KRISTOFF CONTINUE UP THE MOUNTAIN.

PAUSING TO CATCH HER BREATH, ANNA LOOKS DOWN TO SEE...
GASP

ARENDELLE.
IT'S COMPLETELY FROZEN.

...BUT IT'LL BE FINE. ELSA WILL THAW IT.
WILL SHE?

...YEAH. NOW COME ON. THIS WAY TO THE NORTH MOUNTAIN?

MORE LIKE THIS WAY.

OH...

EVERY SUMMER, THE VALLEY AT THE BASE OF THE MOUNTAIN IS FILLED WITH FLOWERS AND BIRDS SINGING IN THE WARM SUNSHINE...

...ALMOST EVERY SUMMER...

I NEVER KNEW WINTER COULD BE SO BEAUTIFUL.
YEAH... IT REALLY IS BEAUTIFUL, ISN'T IT?

BUT IT'S SO WHITE, YOU KNOW?

??
??

HOW ABOUT A LITTLE COLOR?

I'M THINKING, LIKE, MAYBE SOME CRIMSON...
...OR CHARTREUSE...

HOW 'BOUT YELLOW....

NO, NOT YELLOW.
YELLOW AND SNOW? BRRR - NO GO.

AM I RIGHT?

AAGGGHH!

HI!
YOU'RE CREEPY.

WHOAAA!

I DON'T WANT IT!

BACKATCHA.

NO!
PLEASE DON'T DROP ME.

COME ON, IT'S JUST A HEAD.

EW, EW, EW THE BODY!

UM, WE GOT OFF TO A BAD START...

GO BACK TO YOUR BODY!
WHAM!
OH! OKAY!

NOW WE CAN - WAIT.
WHAT AM I LOOKING AT RIGHT NOW?

WHY ARE YOU HANGING OFF THE EARTH LIKE A BAT?

...OKAY. WAIT ONE SECOND.

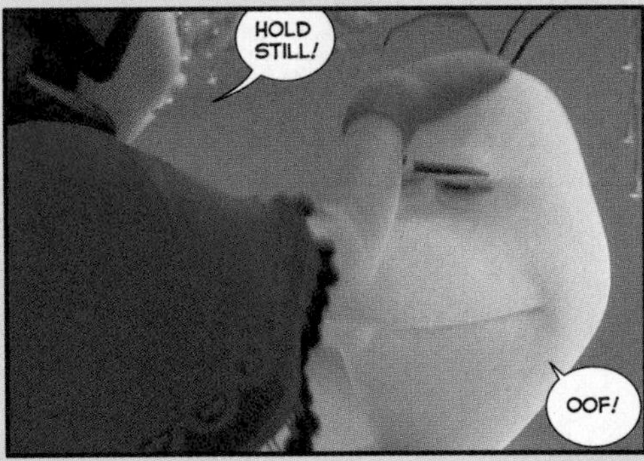
HOLD STILL!
OOF!

OOOH! THANK YOU!
YOU'RE WELCOME.
NOW I'M PERFECT!

WELL...
ALMOST...

IT WAS LIKE MY WHOLE LIFE GOT TURNED UPSIDE DOWN.

HERE --
OOF!
FOONF

OUCH.

OH! TOO HARD. I'M SORRY. I - I - I WAS JUST...
HEAD RUSH!

ARE YOU OKAY?
ARE YOU KIDDING ME?
I - AM WONDERFUL!
I'VE WANTED A NOSE!

SO CUTE. IT'S LIKE A LITTLE BABY UNICORN.

I CAN FIX THIS --!
WHACK!
OOH!

WHAT? HEY! WHOA!

OH, I LOVE IT EVEN MORE! HAH... ALL RIGHT...

...LET'S START THIS THING OVER.
HI EVERYONE. I'M OLAF. AND I LIKE WARM HUGS.

OLAF...?
...THAT'S RIGHT, OLAF.

...AND YOU ARE?
OH, UM... I'M ANNA.
AND WHO'S THE FUNKY-LOOKING DONKEY OVER THERE?

THAT'S SVEN.
UH-HUH. AND WHO'S THE REINDEER?
...SVEN
OH. THEY'RE--OH, OKAY... MAKES THINGS EASIER FOR ME.

HA. AW, THAT'S SWEET -- HE WANTS TO KISS MY NOSE.

I LIKE YOU, TOO!

OLAF, DID ELSA BUILD YOU?
YEAH. WHY?

DO YOU KNOW WHERE SHE IS?
YEAH! WHY?
FASCINATING...

DO YOU THINK YOU COULD SHOW US THE WAY?
...HOW DOES THIS WORK --?
WHACK!

STOP IT, SVEN. TRYING TO FOCUS HERE.
YEAH, WHY?

I'LL TELL YOU WHY. WE NEED ELSA TO BRING BACK SUMMER.
SUMMER!!
OH, I DON'T KNOW WHY BUT I'VE ALWAYS LOVED THE IDEA OF SUMMER, AND SUN, AND ALL THINGS HOT.

REALLY? I'M GUESSING YOU DON'T HAVE MUCH EXPERIENCE WITH HEAT.
NOPE. BUT SOMETIMES I LIKE TO CLOSE MY EYES...

...AND IMAGINE
WHAT IT'D BE LIKE
WHEN SUMMER
DOES COME.

"I CAN SEE IT ALL NOW--
I'D START MY DAY IN A
BEAUTIFUL FIELD!

"THE BEES
ARE OUT
BUZZ
BUZZ
BUZZ!

"I MIGHT EVEN FIND
A DANDELION, AND
MAKE A WISH ON THE --

AAA-
CHOOO!

"...MAKE A WISH
ON THE FUZZ.
AHEM

"AND THAT'S
JUST FOR
STARTERS...

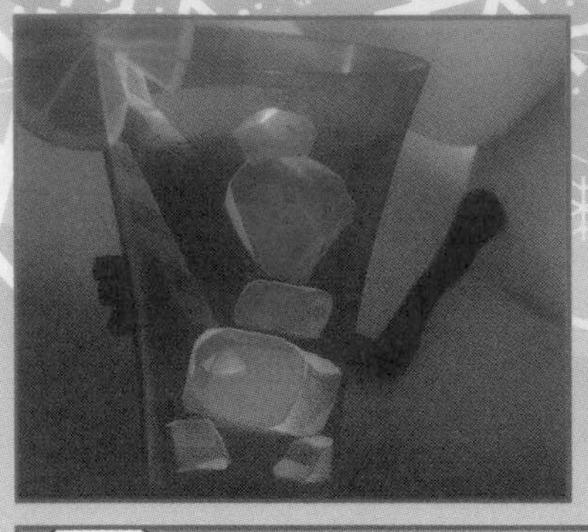

"...BECAUSE THEN I'M HEADING TO THE BEACH.

OH! I COULD GET A TAN! I'VE ALWAYS WANTED A TAN.

IT'D BE A GREAT LOOK FOR ME.

OHHHH, YEAH.

"AND THEN THERE'S SAILING...

"...WHICH WOULD BE SO MUCH EASIER ON UNFROZEN WAVES!

"AND SO WOULD SWIMMING!
WHEE
SPLASH

WHO KNEW I'D BE SO GREAT AT FLOATING?

"THEN I'LL GET BACK TO THE SHORE AND SEE...

"ALL OF MY FRIENDS, JUST WAITING FOR ME.
CAN I BORROW YOUR HAT?

IT'LL BE A COOL TIME ON A WARM DAY--
WHEN I FINALLY SEE SUMMER...!

FULL OF DANCING AND PLAYING ON THE BOARDWALK!

"I KNOW HOW MUCH FOLKS LOVE WARM THINGS IN THE WINTER...
"SO SUMMER MUST REALLY BE GREAT!

IT'LL BE SO WONDERFUL ...

WHEN I FINALLY GET TO EXPERIENCE MY VERY FIRST HOT, SUNNY DAY...

WHEN THAT DAY COMES, I'M GOING TO BE...

ONE HAPPY SNOWMAN!

BUT THAT'S MY DREAM.

TO RELAX...

TO ENJOY...

JUST LET OFF SOME STEAM!

SUCH PRETTY CLOUDS...

PERFECT-- PICNIC WEATHER. WHICH IS SOMETHING ELSE I WANT TO DO
A PICNIC WOULD BE PERFECT --

--AND YOU GUYS CAN COME, TOO

YOU CAN BE THERE TO SEE THE LOOK ON MY FACE...

WHEN I FINALLY FIND MY WAY INTO SUMMER!

HE DOESN'T KNOW, DOES HE? I GOTTA TELL HIM.
DON'T EVEN THINK ABOUT IT.

IT'S WHAT I DREAM OF --

--SOME DAY I'LL SEE IT!

THE GREEN! THE WARM! I'M READY-

-- FOR SUMMER!

SO COME ON! ELSA'S THIS WAY.

HAHA! OKAY, I'M COMING!
LET'S GO BRING BACK SUMMER!

SOMEBODY HAS REALLY GOT TO TELL HIM.

THE MAGICAL WINTER CONTINUES TO HOLD ARENDELLE IN ITS ICY GRIP, AND THE TEMPERS OF ITS CITIZENS ARE STARTING TO RUN HOT.

WHEN FIREWOOD GETS WET, IT WON'T CATCH FIRE. THAT'S WHY YOU STACK IT BARK UP.
BARK DOWN IS DRIER. EVERYBODY KNOWS THAT.

BARK UP.
BARK DOWN.

UP! OOOOF!
DOWN!
CLOAK!

DOES ANYONE NEED A CLOAK?
ARENDELLE IS INDEBTED TO YOU, YOUR HIGHNESS.

THE CASTLE IS OPEN. THERE'S SOUP AND HOT GLÖGG IN THE GREAT HALL.

GUARD-- OVER HERE.

PLEASE PASS THESE OUT.

PRINCE HANS, ARE WE JUST EXPECTED TO SIT HERE AND FREEZE...
shiver

...WHILE YOU GIVE AWAY ALL OF ARRENDELLE'S TRADABLE GOODS?
PRINCESS ANNA HAS GIVEN HER ORDERS AND--

AND THAT'S ANOTHER THING! HAS IT DAWNED ON YOU THAT YOUR PRINCESS MAY BE CONSPIRING WITH HER WICKED SORCERESS OF A SISTER TO DESTROY US ALL?
DO NOT QUESTION THE PRINCESS!
SHE LEFT ME IN CHARGE, AND I WILL NOT HESITATE TO PROTECT ARENDELLE FROM TREASON.

WHAT? TREASON?? BUT I --
KLOP KLOP KLOP

NEIGH!
LOOK OUT!

WHOA! WHOA, BOY!

EASY. EASY...

PRINCE HANS, WHERE'S PRINCESS ANNA? SHE WAS ON THAT HORSE!
WHAT'S HAPPENED TO HER?

PRINCESS ANNA IS IN TROUBLE.

I NEED VOLUNTEERS TO GO WITH ME TO FIND HER!
I'LL GO!
I VOLUNTEER!

I VOLUNTEER TWO MEN, MY LORD!

BE PREPARED FOR ANYTHING. AND SHOULD YOU ENCOUNTER THE QUEEN...

...YOU ARE TO PUT AN END TO THIS WINTER, DO YOU UNDERSTAND?

SO HOW EXACTLY ARE YOU PLANNING TO STOP THIS WEATHER?
I'M GONNA TALK TO MY SISTER.
THAT'S YOUR PLAN? YOU MEAN MY ICE BUSINESS IS RIDING ON YOU...TALKING TO YOUR SISTER?
YUP.

SO YOU'RE NOT AT ALL...

...AFRAID OF HER?
NO. WHY WOULD I BE?
YEAH, I BET ELSA'S THE NICEST, GENTLEST...

...WARMEST PERSON EVER.

OH, LOOK AT THAT. I'VE BEEN IMPALED.
HAHAHA!

SEVERAL HOURS SPENT TRUDGING THROUGH THE SNOW LATER...

SO WHAT NOW?
I HAVE NO IDEA. IT'S TOO STEEP TO HIKE UP.

I'VE ONLY GOT ONE ROPE, AND YOU DON'T KNOW HOW TO CLIMB MOUNTAINS.

SAYS YOU.

UM..., WHAT ARE YOU DOING?

I'M GOING... *HUFF*...TO SEE MY SISTER
YOU'RE GOING TO KILL YOURSELF. I WOULDN'T PUT MY FOOT THERE, BY THE WAY.
YOU'RE DISTRACTING ME.
OR THERE.

HOW DO YOU KNOW ELSA EVEN WANTS TO SEE YOU?

NOBODY WANTS TO BE ALONE. EXCEPT MAYBE YOU...

I'M NOT ALONE. I HAVE FRIENDS, REMEMBER?

YOU MEAN THE LOVE EXPERTS?
YES, THE LOVE EXPERTS!

...PLEASE TELL ME I'M ALMOST THERE.
NOT QUITE...

DOES THE AIR
THIN UP HERE TO YOU?

JUST HANG ON--
HEY, SVEN?

NOT SURE IF THIS IS GOING TO SOLVE THE PROBLEM, BUT I FOUND A STAIRCASE THAT LEADS EXACTLY WHERE YOU WANT TO GO

HA HA! THANK GOODNESS!

CATCH!
OOOF!

THANKS!

THAT WAS LIKE A CRAZY TRUST EXERCISE.

THE STAIRS LEAD STRAIGHT UP THE MOUNTAIN.

AND AT THE TOP...

...ELSA'S ICE PALACE.

WHOA.
NOW THAT IS SOME SERIOUS ICE.

I THINK I MIGHT CRY.

GO AHEAD. I WON'T JUDGE. COME ON, OLAF.

I DON'T THINK THAT'S A GOOD IDEA, SVEN...
KLOP
KLOP

SLIP

WHUMP!

TAKE IT EASY. I GOTCHA.

YOU STAY RIGHT HERE, BUDDY.

I JUST CAN'T GET OVER THIS ICE. FLAWLESS.

OKAY. KNOCK.

JUST... KNOCK.

WHY ISN'T SHE KNOCKING? DO YOU THINK SHE KNOWS HOW TO KNOCK?

KNOCK
KNOCK

THE SOUND OF ANNA'S KNOCK ECHOES THROUGHOUT THE PALACE AS THE DOOR SLOWLY BEGINS TO OPEN.

HA. IT OPENED. THAT'S A FIRST.

UM... YOU SHOULD PROBABLY WAIT OUT HERE.

WHAT?!

WELL, IT'S JUST, LAST TIME I INTRODUCED ELSA TO A GUY, SHE FROZE EVERYTHING.
BUT IT'S A PALACE MADE OF ICE. ICE IS MY LIFE!
BYE, SVEN.

YOU TOO, OLAF.
ME?

JUST... GIVE US A MINUTE.
OKAY. ONE... TWO...

...THREE... FOUR....

ANNA GREW UP IN A CASTLE. IT WAS HUGE, WITH HUNDREDS OF ROOMS AND HALLWAYS THAT SEEMED TO GO ON FOREVER.

BUT NOW IT FELT PRACTICALLY TINY. HOW COULD HER SISTER HAVE MADE ALL THIS?

AND THE BEAUTY --
THE BEAUTY TOOK
HER BREATH AWAY.

ELSA?
IT'S ME...

THEN THE ECHO
ANSWERS BACK.

ANNA.

ANNA CAN HARDLY BELIEVE HER
EYES. HER SISTER LOOKS SO
BEAUTIFUL, SO CONFIDENT. LIKE
THIS IS WHAT SHE WAS ALWAYS
MEANT TO BE.

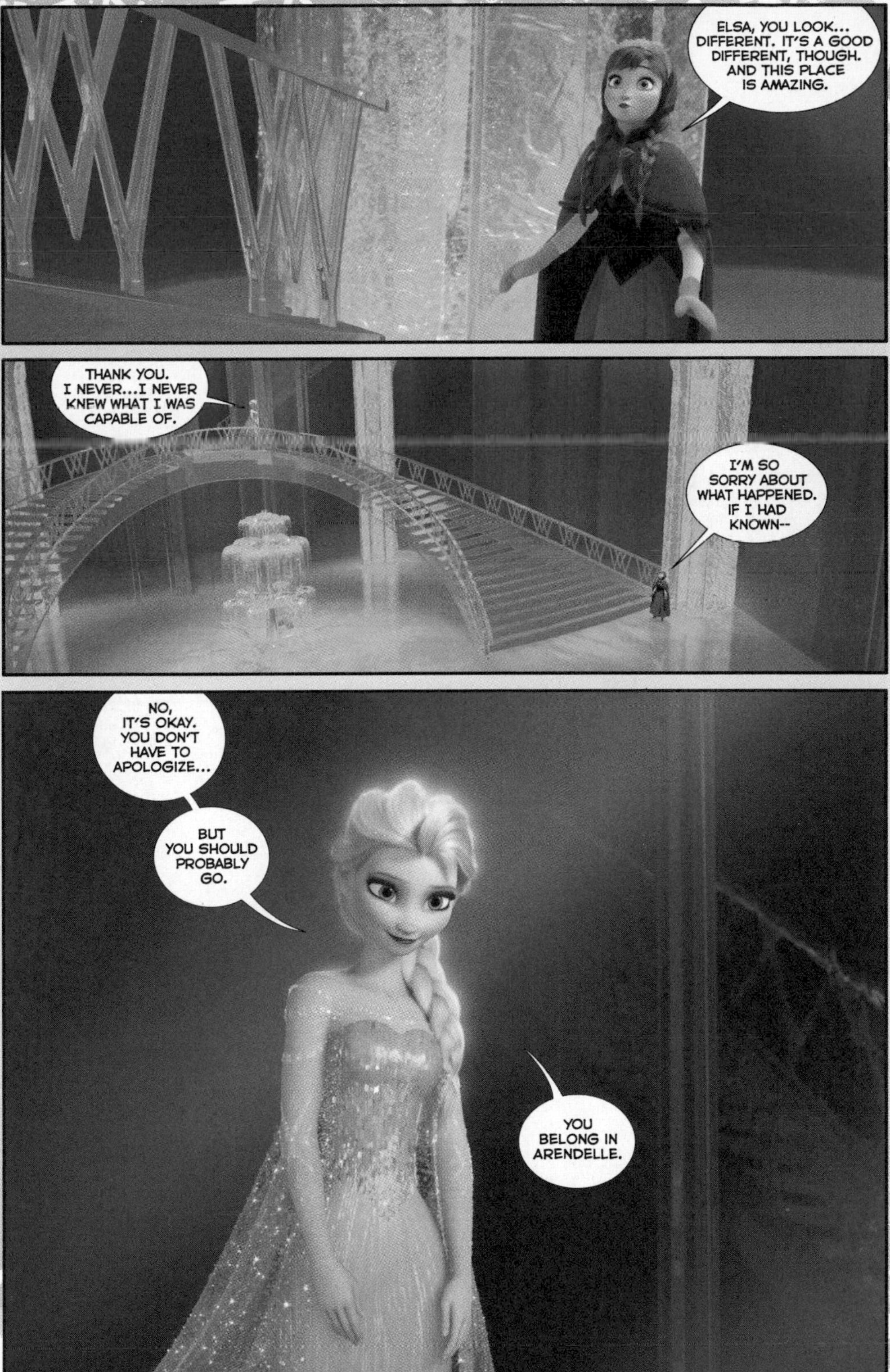

NO, IT'S OKAY. YOU DON'T HAVE TO APOLOGIZE...

BUT YOU SHOULD PROBABLY GO.

YOU BELONG IN ARENDELLE.

SO DO YOU, ELSA.

NO, I BELONG HERE. ALONE.

HERE I CAN BE WHO I AM WITHOUT HURTING ANYBODY.

ACTUALLY, ABOUT THAT...
58...59... 60.

WAIT, WHAT IS THAT?

HI!

I'M OLAF, AND I LIKE WARM HUGS!

OLAF?

BECAUSE IT ALREADY HAPPENED ONCE BEFORE.

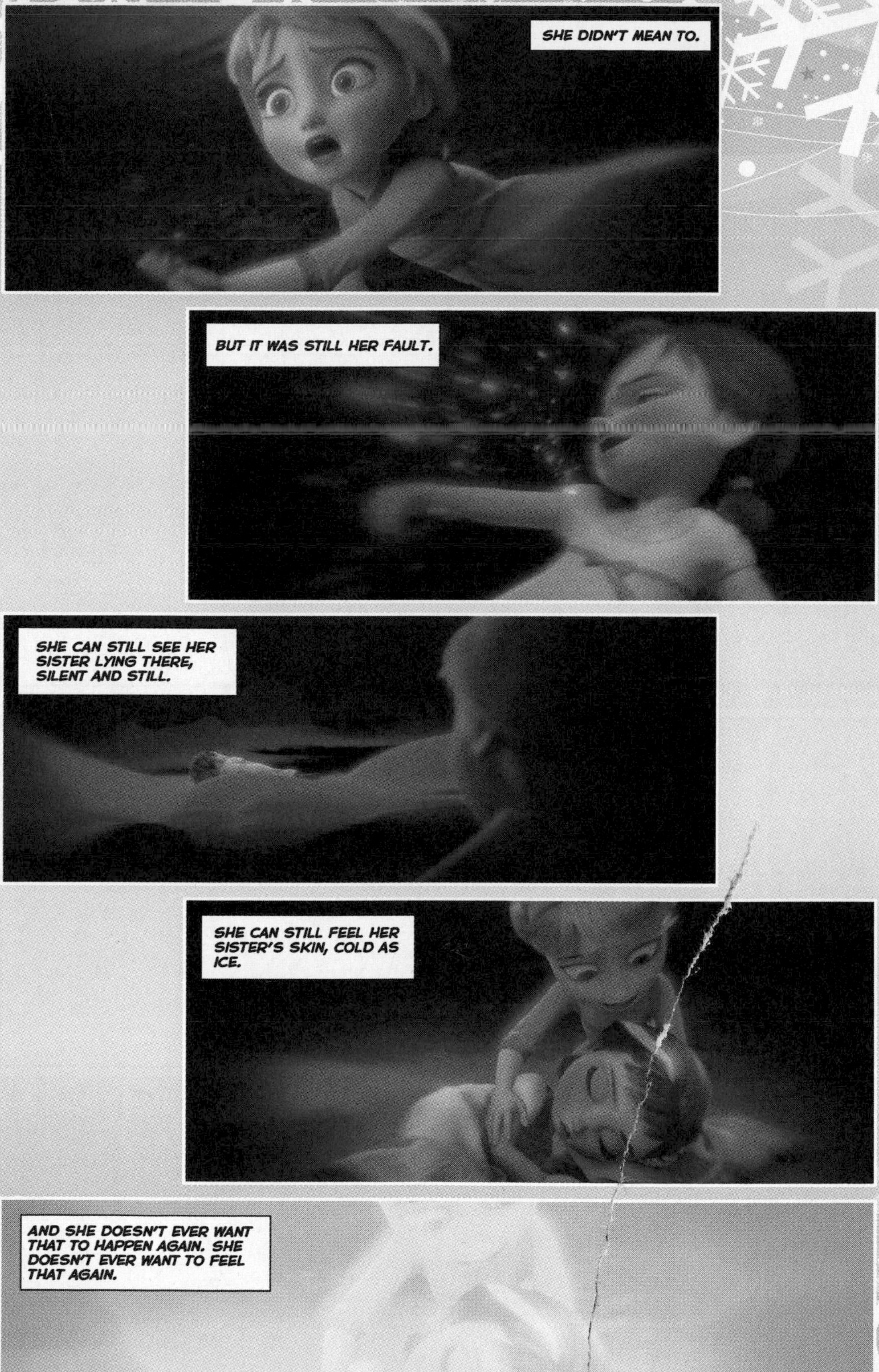

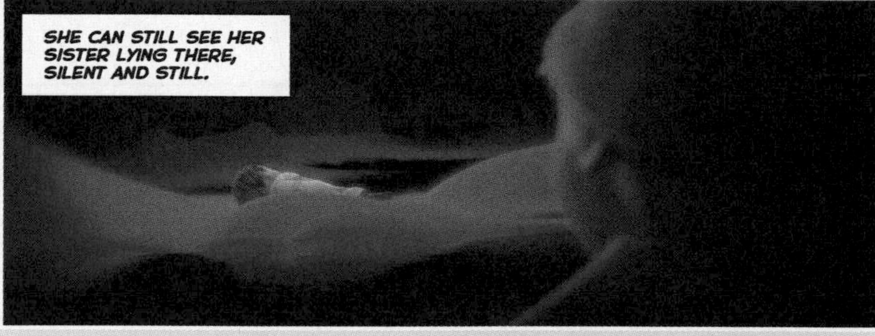

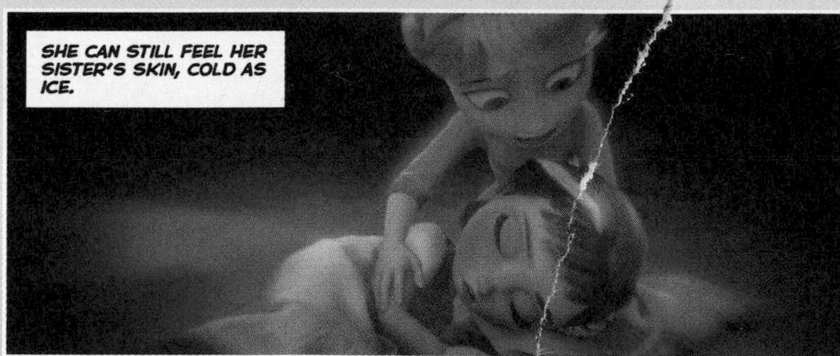

AND SHE DOESN'T EVER WANT THAT TO HAPPEN AGAIN. SHE DOESN'T EVER WANT TO FEEL THAT AGAIN.

NO.
WE CAN'T.
GOODBYE, ANNA.
ELSA, WAIT!
I'M JUST TRYING TO PROTECT YOU!

YOU DON'T HAVE TO PROTECT ME -- I'M NOT AFRAID!

PLEASE DON'T SHUT ME OUT AGAIN!

ELSA!

YOU DON'T HAVE TO STAY AWAY!

YOU DON'T HAVE TO BE SCARED!

I UNDERSTAND; I DO.

AND I KNOW...

...IF YOU COME BACK...

...WE CAN FIX THIS.
TOGETHER.

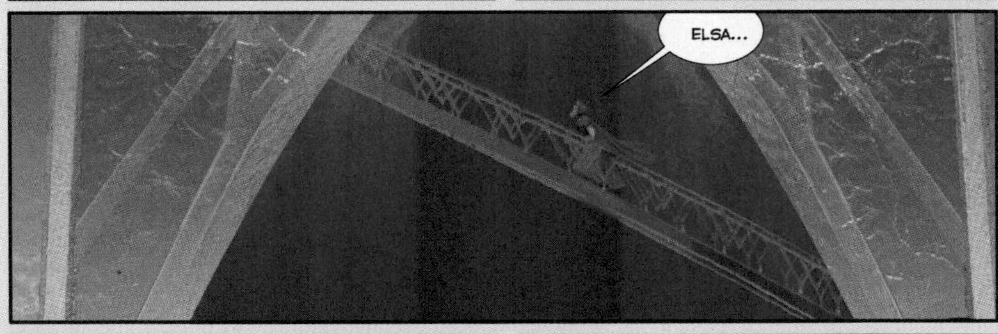
ELSA...

PLEASE COME HOME.

ANNA... I CAN'T.

I'LL BE WITH YOU. I'LL BE RIGHT THERE, ALL THE WAY.

ANNA... YOU HAVE TO GO HOME.

YOU CAN OPEN THE GATES TO THE PEOPLE, LIKE YOU ALWAYS WANTED.
BUT ELSA...

NO BUTS.

I'M HAPPY HERE.

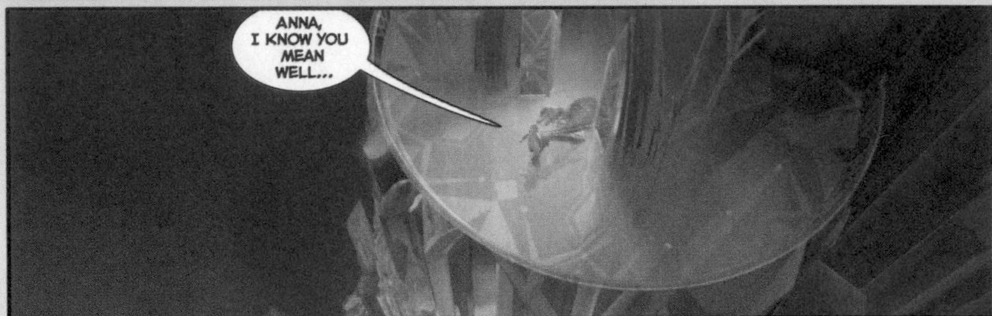
ANNA, I KNOW YOU MEAN WELL...

BUT YOU HAVE TO LEAVE ME BE.

I KNOW I'M ALONE... BUT I'M FINALLY FREE.

...NOW PLEASE, LEAVE ME HERE.

WHERE EVERYONE WILL BE SAFE FROM ME
THAT'S THE THING, ELSA.

WE'RE NOT SAFE.

WHAT DO YOU MEAN?

YOU - YOU REALLY DON'T KNOW?

KNOW WHAT?

ARENDELLE'S COVERED IN REALLY DEEP...
...SNOW.
WHAT?
YOU KIND OF SET OFF AN ETERNAL WINTER... EVERYWHERE.
EVERYWHERE?
IT'S OKAY, YOU CAN JUST UNFREEZE IT!
NO I CAN'T, I - I DON'T KNOW HOW!
SURE YOU CAN! I KNOW YOU CAN!

I WAS SUCH A FOOL! I SHOULD HAVE KNOWN I'D NEVER BE FREE.
THERE'S NO ESCAPE FROM MY CURSE.
ELSA --
WE CAN WORK TOGETHER.
WE'LL FIGURE OUT A WAY TO REVERSE THIS STORM!
ANNA, I'LL ONLY MAKE IT WORSE!
DON'T PANIC.
BUT I'M AFRAID!
WE CAN MAKE THIS BETTER.

ANNA, YOU'RE NOT SAFE HERE!
YOU HAVE TO GO!
WE CAN DO THIS, ELSA, TOGETHER!
NO!
WE CAN FIX EVERYTHING!
IT'LL ALL BE --
I CAN'T!
UNGH!
...OH.

...UNH!

...ANNA?

GASP!

ANNA!

ARE YOU OKAY?
I'M OKAY. I'M FINE.

WHO IS THIS?
WAIT, IT DOESN'T MATTER -- JUST...

YOU HAVE TO GO.
NO. I KNOW WE CAN FIGURE THIS OUT TOGETHER!

HOW? WHAT POWER DO YOU HAVE TO STOP THIS WINTER? TO STOP ME?
ANNA, I THINK WE SHOULD GO.
NO. I'M NOT LEAVING WITHOUT YOU, ELSA!

YES, YOU ARE.

FWOOSH
RRRUMMMBLLLEE

WHAT A CUTE MARSHMALLOW SNOWMAN!
GASP!

HRRRRRRR

STOP! PUT US DOWN!

GO AWAY!

WHOOAAAAH!!

SNORT.

HEADS UP!

SPLAT
OH!

WATCH OUT FOR MY BUTT!

SPLORTCH
SPLAT

IT IS NOT NICE TO THROW PEOPLE!

WHOA-WHOA-WHOA-WHOA, THERE, FEISTY PANTS. RELAX. LET THE MARSHMALLOW SNOWMAN BE.
LET ME AT HIM! I WANT TO GET HIM! I --

OKAY. I'M CALM.

HEEEYAH!
OH, COME ON!
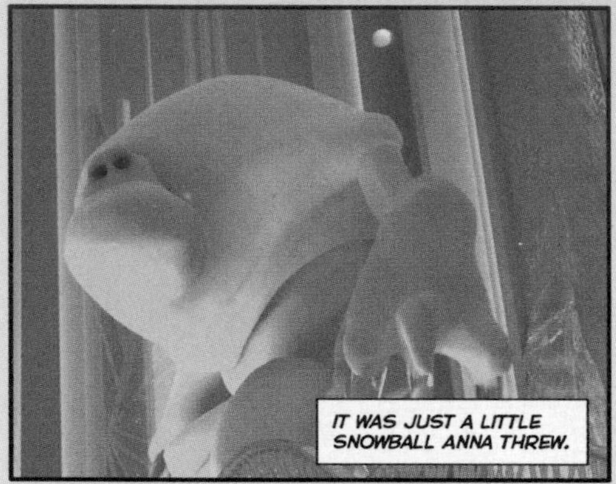
IT WAS JUST A LITTLE SNOWBALL ANNA THREW.
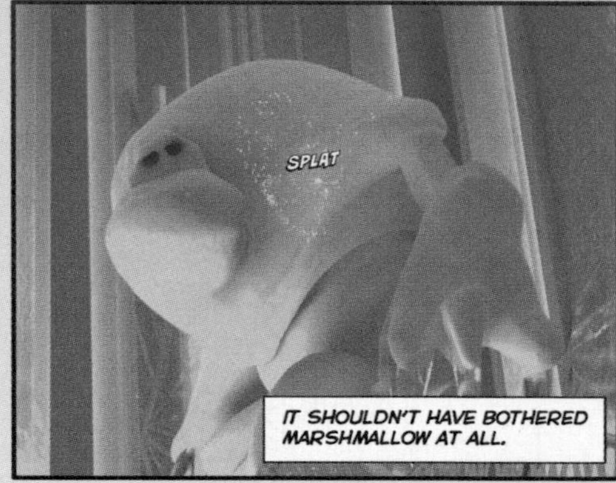
SPLAT
IT SHOULDN'T HAVE BOTHERED MARSHMALLOW AT ALL.

HRRRAAAAAGHHH!

OH, SEE? NOW YOU MADE HIM MAD!
I'LL DISTRACT HIM. YOU GUYS GO.

WAIT, NO, NOT YOU GUYS, WHOOP---

THIS JUST GOT A WHOLE LOT HARDER.
SPLAT

WHOOOOP!

GRRAAAAAAARRR!

WHOOOAAAAHHH!!!

DOWN THE MOUNTAIN KRISTOFF AND ANNA GO, PICKING UP SPEED, BOTH THINKING THE SAME THING...

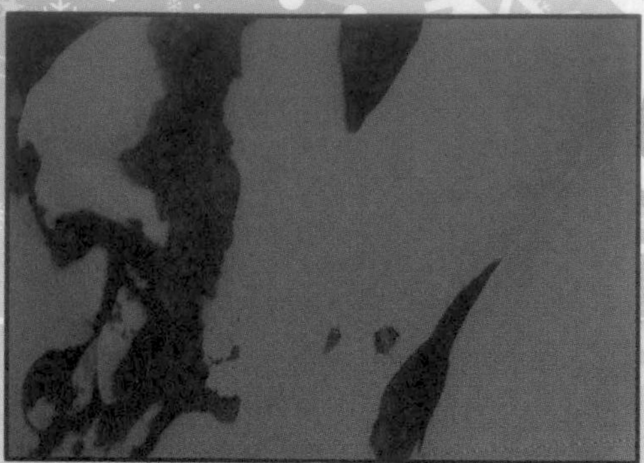

"WE HAVE TO OUTRUN THAT GIGANTIC MONSTER SNOWMAN."

HRRRAAAAAGHH!
WHAM

RUN!

THEY RUN FOR ALL THEY'RE WORTH...

...WITH MARSHMALLOW FOLLOWING CLOSE BEHIND, AND GETTING CLOSER.

THEY NEED A PLAN... AND ANNA COMES UP WITH ONE.

WHAT ARE YOU DOING WITH THAT TREE??
WATCH!

SPLA-BLAAAMM!
GOT HIM! HAHAHA!

WHOA-
WHOAH!

IT'S A
HUNDRED
FOOT
DROP!

IT'S
TWO
HUNDRED.

OW!
THAT'S
TIGHT!

WHAT'S
THAT FOR?
I'M
DIGGING A
SNOW
ANCHOR!

OKAY...

WHAT IF WE FALL?
THERE'S TWENTY FEET OF FRESH POWDER DOWN THERE --

IT'LL BE LIKE LANDING ON A PILLOW.
HOPEFULLY.
TOOM TOOMTOOM

HHHRRRRROOOOOOAAAAAAARRRRRR

OK, ANNA. ON THREE.
OKAY. YOU TELL ME WHEN...
ONE...

"I'M READY TO GO."

I WAS BORN READY! YES!
CALM DOWN.
TWO...

TREE!!

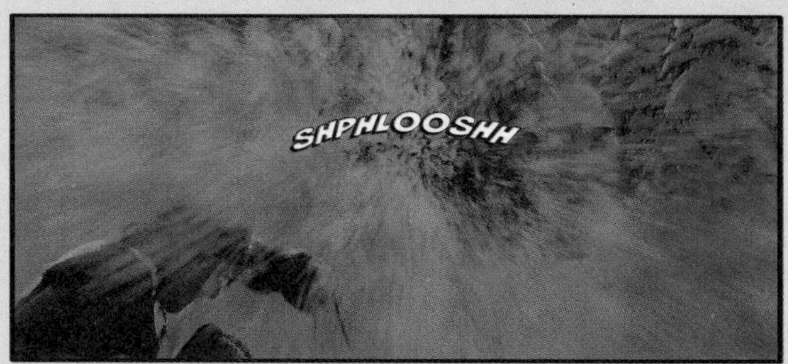
SHPHLOOSHH

WHAT THE--

WHOA!!

SKRICH

OOF!
...THAT HAPPENED.

AH.
AH.
MAN, I AM OUT OF SHAPE.

THERE WE GO.

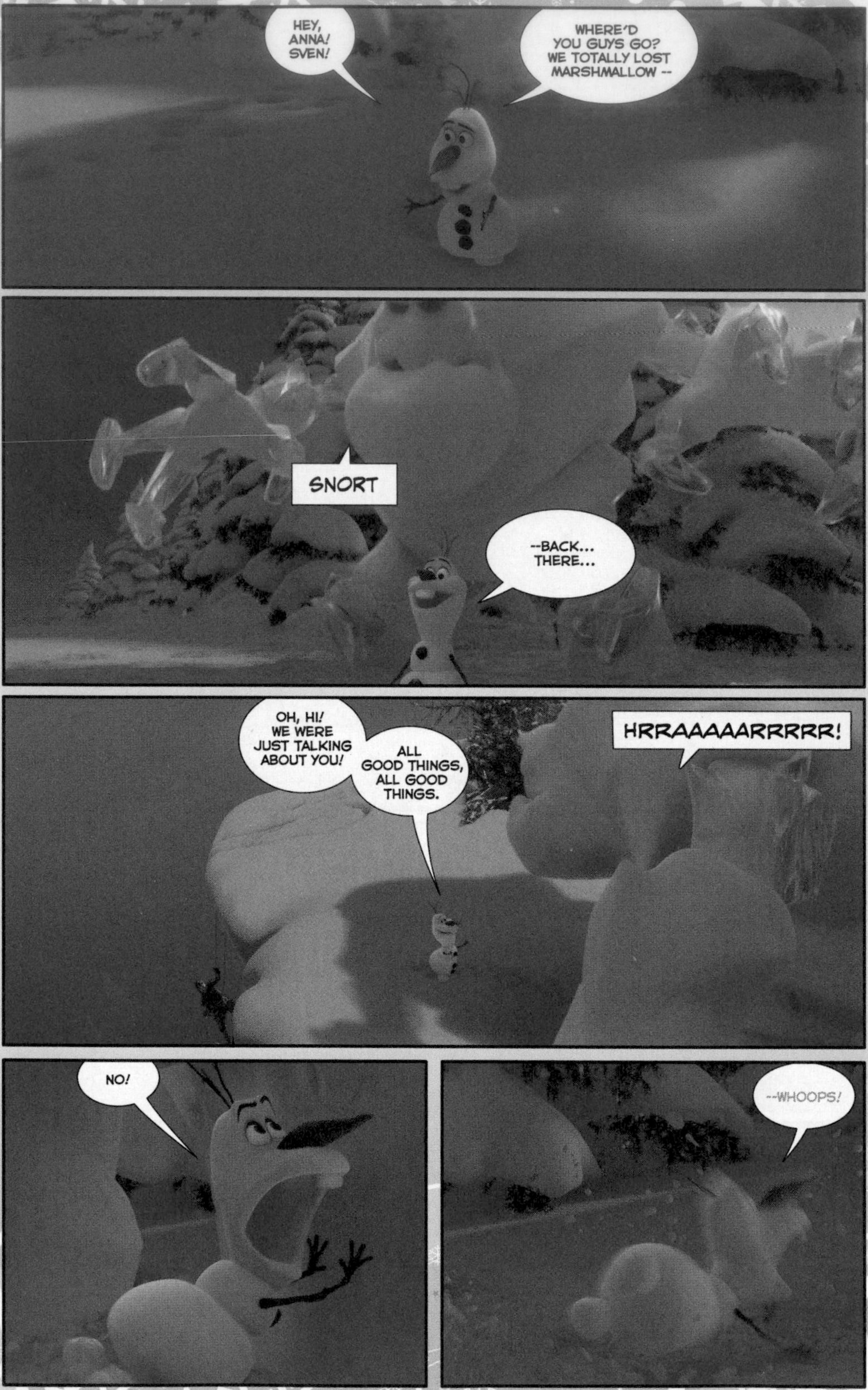

HEY, ANNA! SVEN!
WHERE'D YOU GUYS GO? WE TOTALLY LOST MARSHMALLOW --
SNORT
--BACK... THERE...
OH, HI! WE WERE JUST TALKING ABOUT YOU!
ALL GOOD THINGS, ALL GOOD THINGS.
HRRAAAAARRRRR!

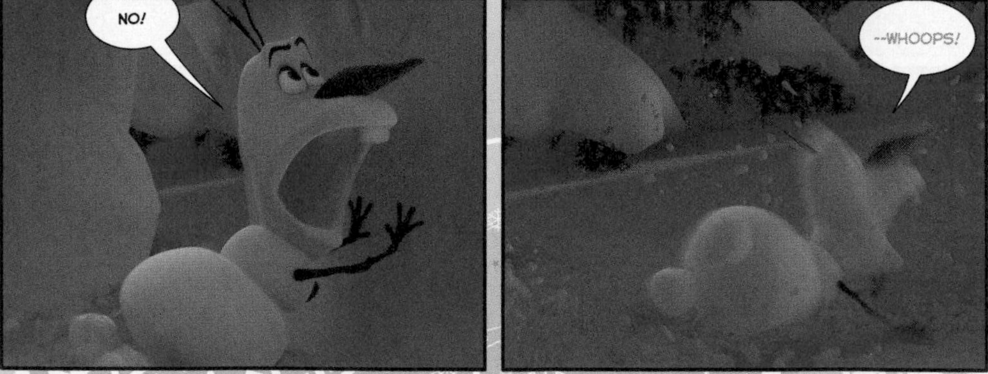

NGH! NGH!
THIS IS NOT MAKING MUCH OF A DIFFERENCE.
GRRRRRRR---
TUMP
WHOOOOA!
OLAF!
PLOOF!
GRRRRR!

HANG IN THERE, GUYS!

YOINK
WAIT, WHAT?
WHAT'S HAPPENING?

KRISTOFF DIDN'T NEED TO ANSWER... THEY COULD BOTH SEE MARSHMALLOW HAULING THEM BACK UP THE MOUNTAIN.

...AND NOT GENTLY.
BONK!
AAAOOOWWW!

KRISTOFF!!

GRRAAARRR!

DON'T COME BACK!

...
WE... WE WON'T.
BEFORE MARSHMALLOW CAN DO ANYTHING ELSE, ANNA SLICES THE ROPE WITH A SMALL KNIFE.

WHOOOAAAAAAAAAA----!!

HRMPH.

--AAAAAAAAAAAAAAA--
FOOMF

HEY, YOU WERE RIGHT! JUST LIKE A PILLOW.

I CAN'T FEEL MY LEGS...
I CAN'T FEEL MY LEGS!!

PTUI-
THOSE ARE MY LEGS.
OOOH. HEY, DO ME A FAVOR.

YEAH, THAT FEELS BETTER.

SNIFF
SNIFF

GASP
HEY, SVEN!

CHOMP
LOOK! HE FOUND US!

AW, WHO'S MY CUTE LITTLE REINDEER?

HEE!
DON'T TALK TO HIM LIKE THAT.

NNFFF--

HERE.
OH! WHOA.

YOU OKAY?
THANK YOU.

UM... HOW'S YOUR HEAD?

AH! OW!
IT'S FINE, AH... I'M GOOD.

HA. IT'S FINE.
I'VE GOT A THICK SKULL.

I DON'T HAVE A SKULL.
...OR BONES.

...SO.
NOW WHAT?

NOW WHAT?

NOW WHAT?! OH!
WHAT AM I GONNA DO? SHE THREW ME OUT. I CAN'T GO BACK TO ARENDELLE WITH THE WEATHER LIKE THIS.
AND THEN THERE'S YOUR ICE BUSINESS--

HEY, DON'T WORRY ABOUT MY ICE BUSINESS... WORRY ABOUT-- YOUR HAIR?!?

WHAT? I JUST FELL OFF A CLIFF. YOU SHOULD SEE YOUR HAIR.
NO, YOURS IS TURNING WHITE.

WHITE? IT'S WHAT?
DOES IT LOOK BAD?
...
NO.

YOU HESITATED.

NO, I DIDN'T.
ANNA, YOU NEED HELP. NOW COME ON.
OKAY! WHERE ARE WE GOING?

TO SEE MY FRIENDS.
THE LOVE EXPERTS?

YES. AND DON'T WORRY; THEY'LL BE ABLE TO FIX THIS.
HOW DO YOU KNOW?
...BECAUSE I'VE SEEN THEM DO IT BEFORE.

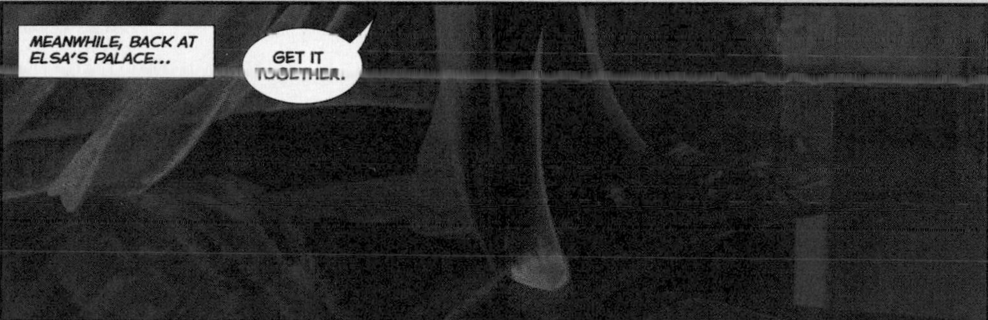
MEANWHILE, BACK AT ELSA'S PALACE...
GET IT TOGETHER.

CONTROL IT. DON'T FEEL.

DON'T FEEL.

DON'T!
FEEL!

A CREAKING AND CRACKLING INTERRUPTS ELSA.
CRAK!
POP!

CRAKLE
CRAK!
IT GROWS LOUDER, AND WHEN IT IS DONE...

...THERE IS MORE ICE THAN EVER.

MEANWHILE, IN THE MOUNTAINS.
LOOK, SVEN...
THE SKY'S AWAKE.

HFF HFF
ARE YOU COLD?

...A
LITTLE.
WAIT. COME
HERE.
OOOH...
THAT'S
NICE.
STEAM VENT.
THERE ARE
MORE ALONG
THE WAY.
SO...
ABOUT MY
FRIENDS.

WELL, I SAY FRIENDS, THEY'RE MORE LIKE FAMILY.
ANYWAY, WHEN I WAS A KID, IT WAS JUST ME AND SVEN, UNTIL THEY TOOK ME IN.
THEY DID?
YEAH.
I DON'T WANT TO SCARE YOU, BUT THEY CAN BE A LITTLE BIT INAPPROPRIATE...
AND LOUD... VERY LOUD...
THEY'RE ALSO STUBBORN AT TIMES, AND A LITTLE OVERBEARING.
AND HEAVY. REALLY, REALLY HEAVY. BUT THEY'RE FINE. YOU'LL GET IT.
THEY MEAN WELL.
KRISTOFF, THEY SOUND WONDERFUL.
OKAY, THEN --
--MEET MY FAMILY.

...THEY'RE ROCKS.
HE'S CRAZY.
HEY GUYS!

WOW, I DIDN'T EVEN RECOGNIZE YOU, YOU'VE LOST SO MUCH WEIGHT!
I'LL DISTRACT HIM WHILE YOU RUN.

HI, SVEN'S FAMILY! IT'S NICE TO MEET YOU!

ANNA, BECAUSE I LOVE YOU, I INSIST YOU RUN.

I UNDERSTAND YOU'RE LOVE EXPERTS!

WHY AREN'T YOU RUNNING?
UM...

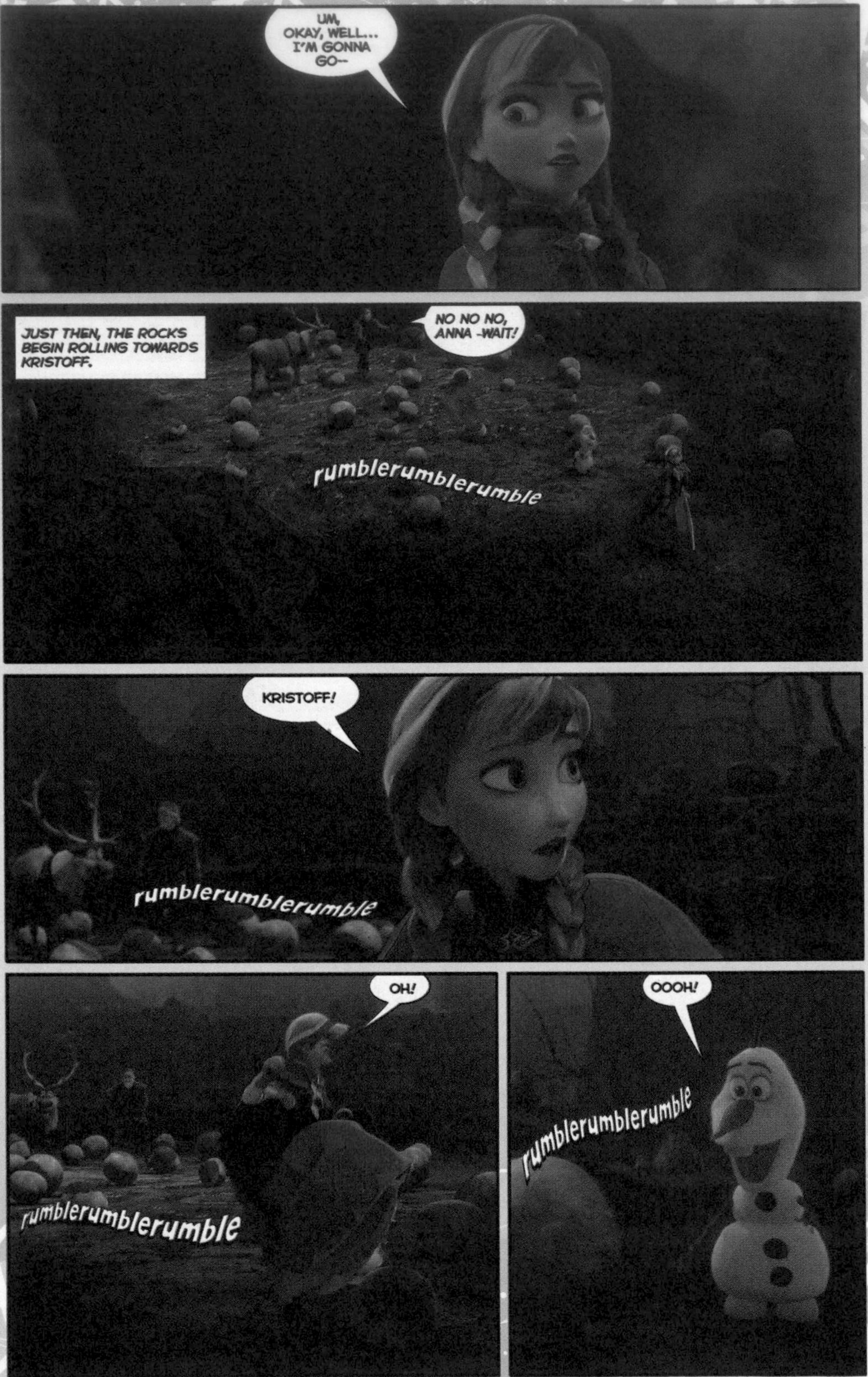

JUST THEN, THE ROCKS BEGIN ROLLING TOWARDS KRISTOFF.

NO NO NO, ANNA -WAIT!

rumblerumblerumble

rumblerumblerumble

rumblerumblerumble

KRISTOFF'S HOME!
IT'S BEEN TOO LONG!

KRISTOFF'S HOME!

WAIT -- WHO IS KRISTOFF?

OH, LET ME LOOK AT YOU!

HEY!
TAKE OFF YOUR CLOTHES, KRISTOFF. I WASH THEM!

AH! NO!
I'M GONNA KEEP MY CLOTHES ON.

KRISTOFF, PICK ME UP!

OOF! YOU'RE GETTING BIG! GOOD FOR YOU!

TROLLS?
PICK ME UP, TOO!

HE BROUGHT A GIRL?

HE BROUGHT A GIRL?
HE BROUGHT A GIRL?
HE BROUGHT A GIRL?
HE BROUGHT A GIRL?
HE BROUGHT A GIRL?

OH!

WHAT'S GOING ON?

I'VE JUST LEARNED TO ROLL WITH IT.
LET ME SEE YOU!

BRIGHT EYES...
...WORKING NOSE...

...STRONG TEETH...
...YES, YES, YES. SHE'LL DO NICELY FOR OUR KRISTOFF.

WAIT.
OH. UM.
NO.
YOU'VE
GOT THE WRONG
IDEA. THAT'S NOT WHY
I BROUGHT
HER HERE.
RIGHT!
WE'RE NOT -ER-
I'M NOT --
UM...
AHEH...
WHAT'S
THE ISSUE,
DEAR?
WHY
ARE YOU HOLDING
BACK FROM
SUCH A
MAN?
IS IT
BECAUSE HE
WALKS KIND OF
CLUMPY?
OR THE
WAY HE GETS
A LITTLE
GRUMPY?

OR MAYBE IT'S HIS FEET?

THEY ARE KIND OF SQUARE-SHAPED. AND POINTY.

I WOULDN'T BLAME YOU IF YOU THOUGHT THEY WERE WEIRD!

MY FEET AREN'T THAT WEIRD.

STILL NOT WASHING BEHIND THE EARS, EH?

...HE'S JUST A LITTLE SMELLY. BUT YOU CAN WORK WITH THAT!

AND OUR LITTLE KRISTOFF IS SUCH A SWEETHEART!

GIVE HER A BIG SMILE, DEAR.

IT'S TRUE; HE IS A LITTLE STRANGE...

WHOOP--

WHOA!

OKAY, MAYBE A LOT STRANGE!
MAYBE IT'S BECAUSE HE'S ALWAYS HANGING AROUND WITH THAT REINDEER?

SNRT?

HEE HEE!

CAN WE JUST STOP TALKING ABOUT THIS?! WE'VE GOT A REAL, ACTUAL PROBLEM HERE.
I'LL SAY!

HA HA! TELL ME MORE! TELL ME EVERYTHING!
HE ONLY HAS A BATH ONCE A WEEK.
OKAY, MAYBE NOT EVERYTHING!
HEY!
BUT HE'S GOT A GOOD HEART.
AND ONLY A COUPLE OF BUGS!
NO I DON'T.
BUT HE'S ALSO GOT POTENTIAL!
YOU COULD FIX HIM RIGHT UP!
ENOUGH! SHE'S ENGAGED TO SOMEONE ELSE, OKAY?!
IS THAT SO?
WELL, I DON'T SEE A RING!

AND I'D CALL THAT A SIGN!
YOU'RE BOTH A BIT OFF-KILTER – YOU TWO WERE CLEARLY MEANT FOR EACH OTHER!
WHEN PEOPLE ARE ANGRY OR SCARED, THEY CAN MAKE BAD DECISIONS...
BUT LOVE? THAT CAN BRING OUT THE BEST IN THEM.
WOW.
AND I THINK YOU TWO WILL BRING OUT THE BEST IN EACH OTHER!
WE ALL NEED TO FIND PEOPLE WE CAN LOVE.
FAMILY... FRIENDS... THEY MAKE LIFE BETTER.
THEY MAKE US BETTER!

AND THAT'S THE TRUTH!
SO COME THIS WAY...
...AND LET US FIX YOU TWO UP!
TRUE LOVE.
TRUE LOVE.
IT'S WHY WE ARE HERE.
DO YOU, ANNA, TAKE KRISTOFF TO BE YOUR TROLL-FULLY WEDDED--

WAIT, WHAT?!
YOU'RE GETTING MARRIED.
I--
NGH...
ANNA?
ANNA -- SAY SOMETHING!
UHHHH
SHE'S COLD AS ICE.

JUST THEN, GRAND PABBIE PUSHES HIS WAY THROUGH THE CROWD FOR A CLOSER LOOK.
THERE'S STRANGE MAGIC HERE!
GRAND PABBIE!
BRING HER TO ME, KRISTOFF.
ANNA, YOUR LIFE IS IN DANGER. THERE IS ICE IN YOUR HEART, PUT THERE BY YOUR SISTER.
IF NOT REMOVED, TO SOLID ICE WILL YOU FREEZE, FOREVER.
WHAT...? NO.
BUT... YOU CAN REMOVE IT, RIGHT?
I CANNOT. I'M SORRY, KRISTOFF. IF IT WAS HER HEAD, THAT WOULD BE EASY.
BUT ONLY AN ACT OF TRUE LOVE CAN THAW A FROZEN HEART.
AN ACT OF TRUE LOVE?

A TRUE LOVE'S KISS, PERHAPS?
SMOOCH
ANNA, WE'VE GOT TO GET YOU BACK TO HANS.
...HANS...
PULL US OUT, SVEN.
SNORT.

COME ON, OLAF!
I'M COMING!
LET'S GO KISS HANS!
WHO IS THIS HANS?!

THE NEXT MORNING, AT ELSA'S PALACE.
WE ARE HERE TO FIND PRINCESS ANNA.

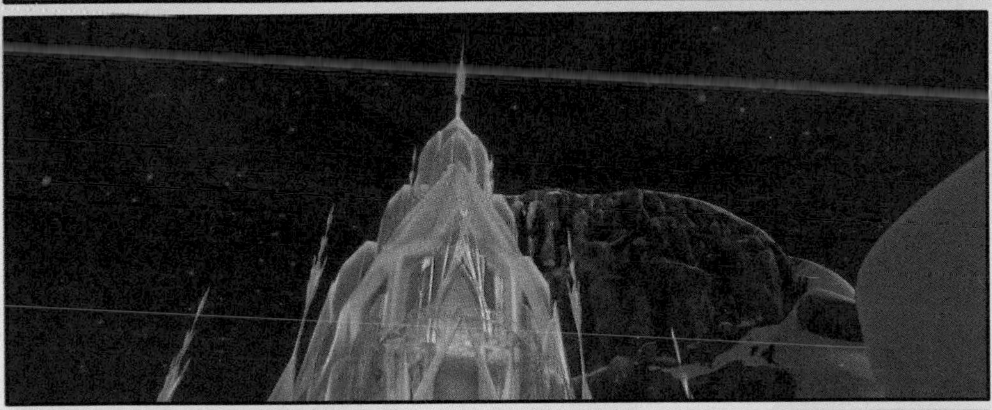

BE ON GUARD, BUT NO HARM IS TO COME TO THE QUEEN.

DO YOU UNDERSTAND?

YES, PRINCE HANS.

HRRAAAAARRRRR!

GO AWAY!

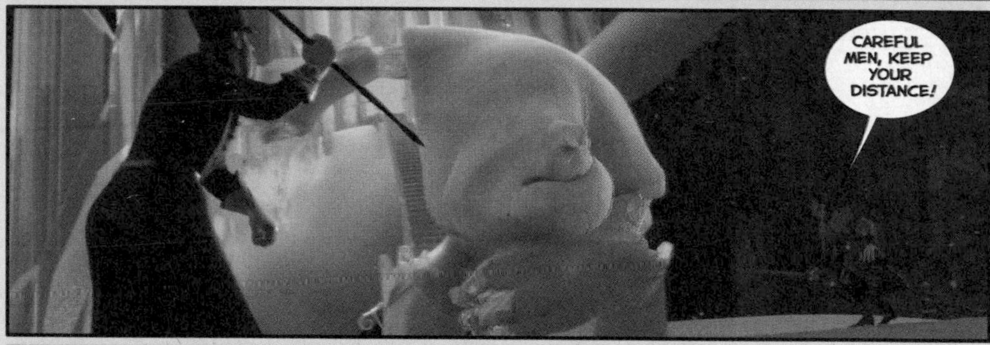
CAREFUL MEN, KEEP YOUR DISTANCE!

GO AWAY!

WHAM

THERE -- IN THE DOORWAY!

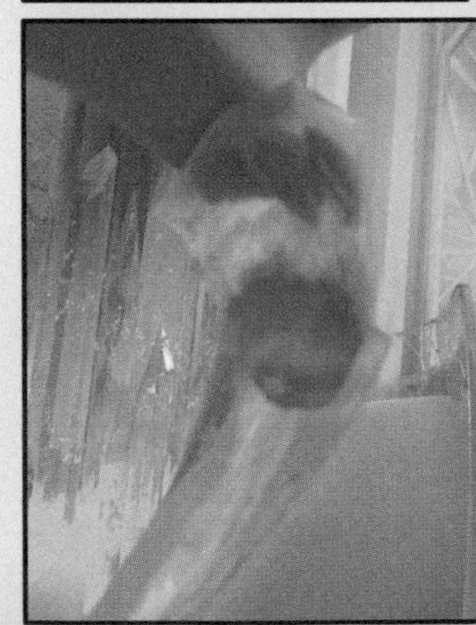

THE QUEEN!

HRRAAAAARRRRR!

WHOA!

AS PRINCE HANS
FACES MARSHMALLOW...

THE DUKE'S THUGS
CHARGE UP THE STAIRS...
GO!
GO!

COME
ON!
...AND PURSUE ELSA TO THE
TOP FLOOR OF HER PALACE.

WATCH YOUR BACK -- NO TELLING WHAT HORRORS SHE HAS IN THIS ICY TOWER!

SHE'S UP THERE - COME ON!

WE GOT HER!

NO... PLEASE.

Tik-Chik

WHISS

SHUNK

FOR A SPLIT SECOND, ELSA STARES AT THE ARROW, TRAPPED IN ICE AND REALIZES.

HELPLESS.
FWOOSH
CRAKCRAKCRAK

SHE CAN DEFEND HERSELF.

STAY AWAY!

GET HER! GET HER!

GO 'ROUND
-- I HAVE HER COVERED HERE!

FWOOSH
CRAKCRAKCRAK

MEANWHILE, OUTSIDE THE ICE PALACE...

HRRAAAAARRRRR!
...PRINCE HANS BARELY DODGES THE CREATURE'S FOOT.
WHAM

HIFF
HIFF

WHISO
HYAH!

HRRRRGGHH?

HRRAAAAAAGHHHH!!!
COME
ON!

GRRRRRRRRR!!

RRAAAAAAARR!

KNASH

HRRRAAAAAAAAAAAAARRRRRR

GASP

HELP HIM UP!

MEANWHILE, IN THE PALACE...

TAKE AIM...

...ELSA IS SURROUNDED.

WITH A PUSH OF
HER POWER...

CREEEEEAK

CRAKCRAKCRAK

GASP
CRACK

STOP MOVING! YOU'LL ONLY HURT YOURSELF!

AS ELSA CONCENTRATES ON THE FIRST GUARD...

...SHE FINDS HERSELF IN THE SIGHTS OF AN EVEN GREATER DANGER...!

FWOOSH
CRAKCRACKCRAK
SUDDENLY...

CRAKCRACKCRAK

...ELSA PUSHES HIM AWAY WITH A WALL OF ICE.

FWOOSH
CRAKCRACKCRAK

CRAKCRA
CRAKCRA

NO--

ELSA'S MAGIC PUSHES HARDER...
FWOOSH

UGH--
CRAKCRA
CRAKCRA

...UNTIL THE DUKE'S GUARD IS PUSHED RIGHT THROUGH THE ICE PALACE'S OUTER WALL.
KR-KRASHHH

AND THEN, SHE PUSHES FURTHER.
CRAKCRA
CRAKCRA

SKRRREEEEE

NFFF--

HF HF
CRAKCRA
CRAKCRAK-K-K

QUEEN ELSA!

QUEEN ELSA. PLEASE.

CRAKCRA CRAKCRA

...DON'T BE THE MONSTER THEY FEAR YOU ARE.

...

FWOOSH
CRAKCRA
CRAKCRA

HANS' WORDS REACH ELSA, AND SHE STOPS. SHE DIDN'T REALLY WANT TO HURT THE GUARDS...

...BUT THEY STILL WANT TO HURT HER.

NO -- !

WHILE HANS IS ABLE TO KNOCK THE CROSSBOW'S AIM OFF...

...THE BOLT FIRES, NOT AT ELSA, BUT UP...

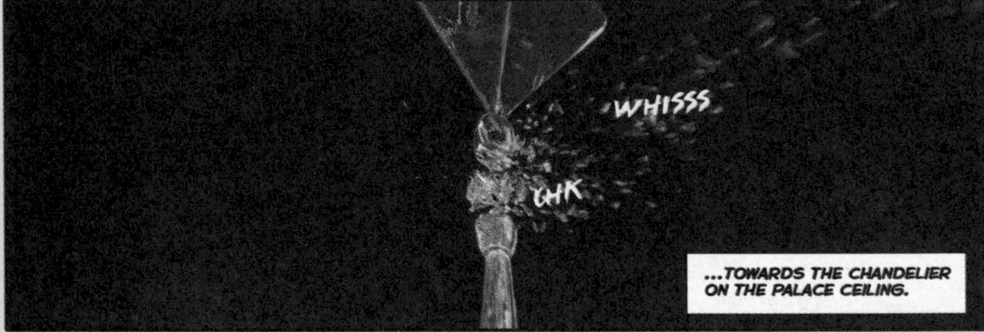
WHISSS
GHK
...TOWARDS THE CHANDELIER ON THE PALACE CEILING.

OH!

CHNK

CHNK
CHNK
CHNK

CHNK
CHNK
CHNK
CHNK

KRKRAS
HHHSHHHH

NNH...

ELSA AWAKENS, SLOWLY, BY THE LIGHT OF A WINDOW IN THE ARENDELLE CASTLE DUNGEON...
AND SHE LOOKS TO SEE WHAT SHE HAS DONE TO ARENDELLE.
KR-CHANK

WHAT--

KR-CHANK-AK

OH, NO...

WHAT HAVE I DONE?
CLICK
CLICK

CREEEAAKKK
YOU! WHY DID YOU BRING ME HERE?
I COULDN'T JUST LET THEM KILL YOU.
BUT I'M A DANGER TO ARENDELLE.
GET ANNA.
ANNA... HAS NOT RETURNED.

IF YOU WOULD JUST STOP THE WINTER AND BRING BACK SUMMER... PLEASE.
DON'T YOU SEE? I... I CAN'T.
YOU HAVE TO TELL THEM TO LET ME GO.
I WILL DO WHAT I CAN.
AND WITH THAT, HANS LEAVES ELSA...
CRACKKAKACK

JUST HANG IN THERE...

C'MON, BUDDY!

FASTER!

SNORT

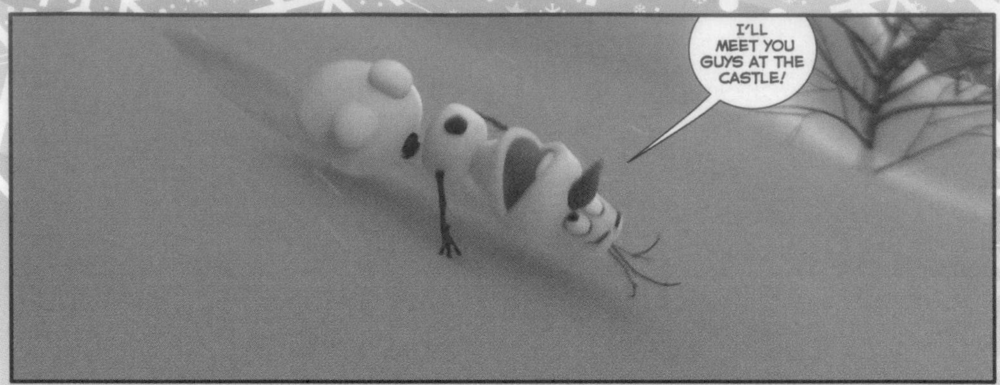
I'LL MEET YOU GUYS AT THE CASTLE!

JUST STAY OUT OF SIGHT, OLAF!
I WILL!

HELLO!

YAAAAH! IT'S ALIVE!

C'MON...

IT'S PRINCESS ANNA!

I'VE GOT YOU.

...ARE YOU G-GONNA BE OKAY?
DON'T WORRY ABOUT ME.

ANNA! OH, YOU HAD US WORRIED SICK!

MY LADY, YOU ARE FREEZING.
YOU POOR GIRL... LET'S GET YOU INSIDE.

GET HER WARM AND FIND PRINCE HANS, IMMEDIATELY.

WE WILL.
THANK YOU.

MAKE SURE SHE'S SAFE!

SLAM

SIGH.

I'M GOING BACK OUT TO LOOK FOR PRINCESS ANNA.
YOU CANNOT RISK GOING OUT THERE AGAIN.
IF ANYTHING HAPPENS TO HER ...
IF ANYTHING HAPPENS TO THE PRINCESS, YOU ARE ALL ARENDELLE HAS LEFT.
HE'S IN HERE. PRINCE HANS.
ANNA!

...YOU'RE SO COLD.
YOU HAVE TO KISS ME.
WHAT?
WE'LL GIVE YOU TWO SOME PRIVACY.
NOW.
HERE WE--
--GO...
COME, SIT -- YOU'RE AS WEAK AS A KITTEN.

WHAT HAPPENED OUT THERE?
ELSA STRUCK ME WITH HER
YOU SAID SHE'D NEVER HURT YOU.
I WAS WRONG...
SHE FROZE MY HEART AND ONLY AN ACT OF TRUE LOVE CAN SAVE ME.
A TRUE LOVE'S KISS.
OH, ANNA...
...IF ONLY THERE WAS SOMEONE OUT THERE WHO LOVED YOU.

...WHAT?
...YOU SAID YOU DID.
AS THIRTEENTH IN LINE IN MY OWN KINGDOM, I DIDN'T STAND A CHANCE. I KNEW I'D HAVE TO MARRY INTO THE THRONE SOMEWHERE...
WHAT ARE YOU TALKING ABOUT?
AS HEIR, ELSA WAS PREFERABLE, OF COURSE. BUT NO ONE WAS GETTING ANYWHERE WITH HER. BUT YOU --

HANS?
YOU WERE SO DESPERATE FOR LOVE YOU WERE WILLING TO MARRY ME...
...JUST LIKE THAT.
I FIGURED, AFTER WE MARRIED, I'D HAVE TO STAGE A LITTLE ACCIDENT FOR ELSA--

HANS, NO...

STOP

BUT THEN SHE DOOMED HERSELF--

--AND YOU WERE DUMB ENOUGH TO GO AFTER HER!

PLEASE.
HEH.
ALL THAT'S LEFT NOW IS TO KILL ELSA AND BRING BACK SUMMER.
YOU'RE NO MATCH FOR ELSA.
NO, YOU'RE NO MATCH FOR ELSA.

I, ON THE OTHER HAND, AM THE HERO WHO IS GOING TO SAVE ARENDELLE FROM DESTRUCTION.
YOU --
YOU WON'T GET AWAY WITH THIS.
OH, I ALREADY HAVE.
click
PLEASE - SOMEBODY HELP...
PLEASE... PLEASE...

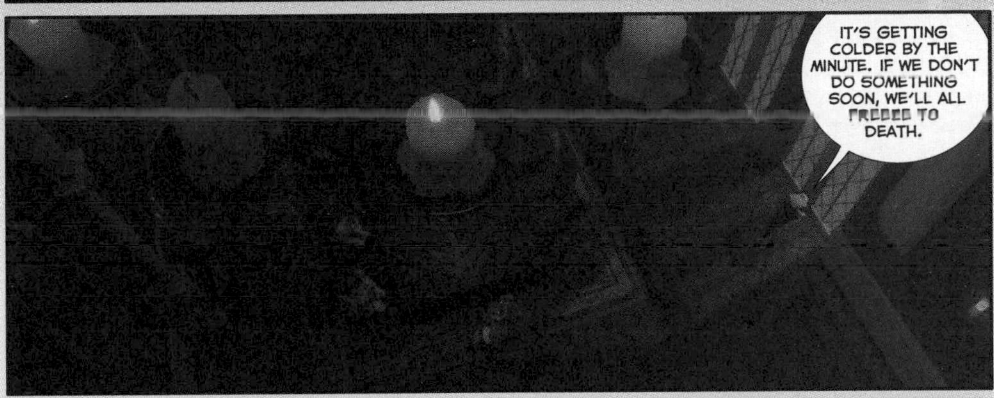

IT'S GETTING COLDER BY THE MINUTE. IF WE DON'T DO SOMETHING SOON, WE'LL ALL FREEZE TO DEATH.

PRINCE HANS!

PRINCESS ANNA... IS DEAD.

WHAT?
NO!
MON DIEU!

WHAT HAPPENED TO HER?

SHE WAS KILLED...
...BY QUEEN ELSA.

HER OWN SISTER!

AT LEAST WE GOT TO SAY OUR MARRIAGE VOWS... BEFORE SHE DIED IN MY ARMS.

THERE CAN BE NO DOUBT NOW; QUEEN ELSA IS A MONSTER AND WE ARE ALL IN GRAVE DANGER.

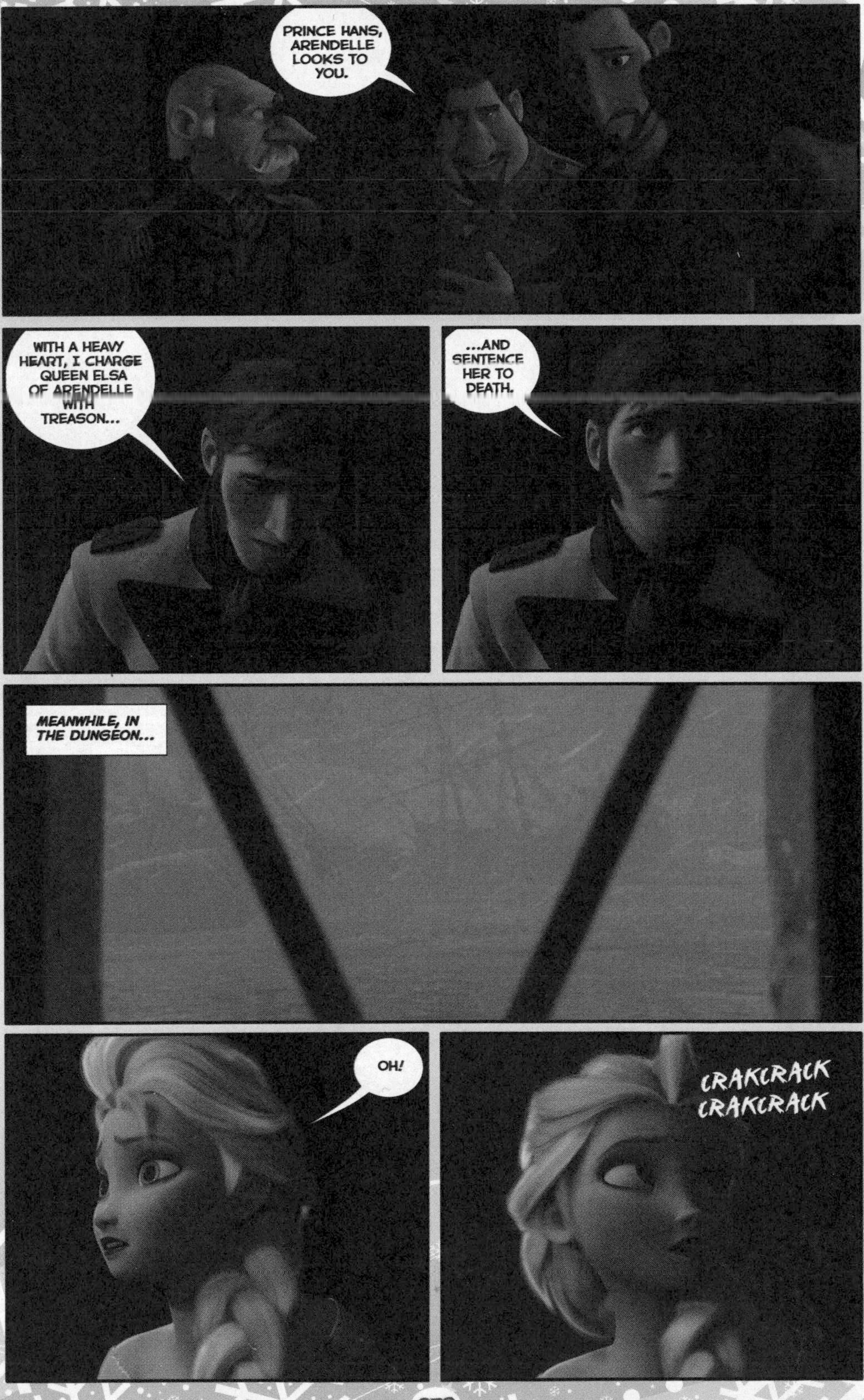

PRINCE HANS, ARENDELLE LOOKS TO YOU.

WITH A HEAVY HEART, I CHARGE QUEEN ELSA OF ARENDELLE WITH TREASON...

...AND SENTENCE HER TO DEATH.

MEANWHILE, IN THE DUNGEON...

CRAKCRACK

CRAKCRACK

MOVE QUICKLY!

NNNNNGH!
QUICKLY!
CRAKCRACK
CRAKCRACK

IT WON'T OPEN! IT'S FROZEN SHUT!
PUSH!

HYAH!

GASP!

PRINCE HANS CAN ONLY GRUNT IN ANGER...

BECAUSE ELSA
HAS ESCAPED.

AWWWF

SNORT

SNRRT!

WHAT IS IT, BUDDY?

HEY! WATCH IT!

WHAT'S WRONG WITH YOU?

SNFF.

BRAAAAW!

I DON'T UNDERSTAND YOU WHEN YOU TALK LIKE THAT.

AAAH!

STOP IT! PUT ME DOWN!

PFFFT.

BRAWW!

NO, SVEN, WE ARE NOT GOING BACK.

--SHE'S WITH HER TRUE LOVE.

SIGH

WHOOOOOSHHHHHHH

WHAT THE --

ANNA!

SNRRT!

GO!

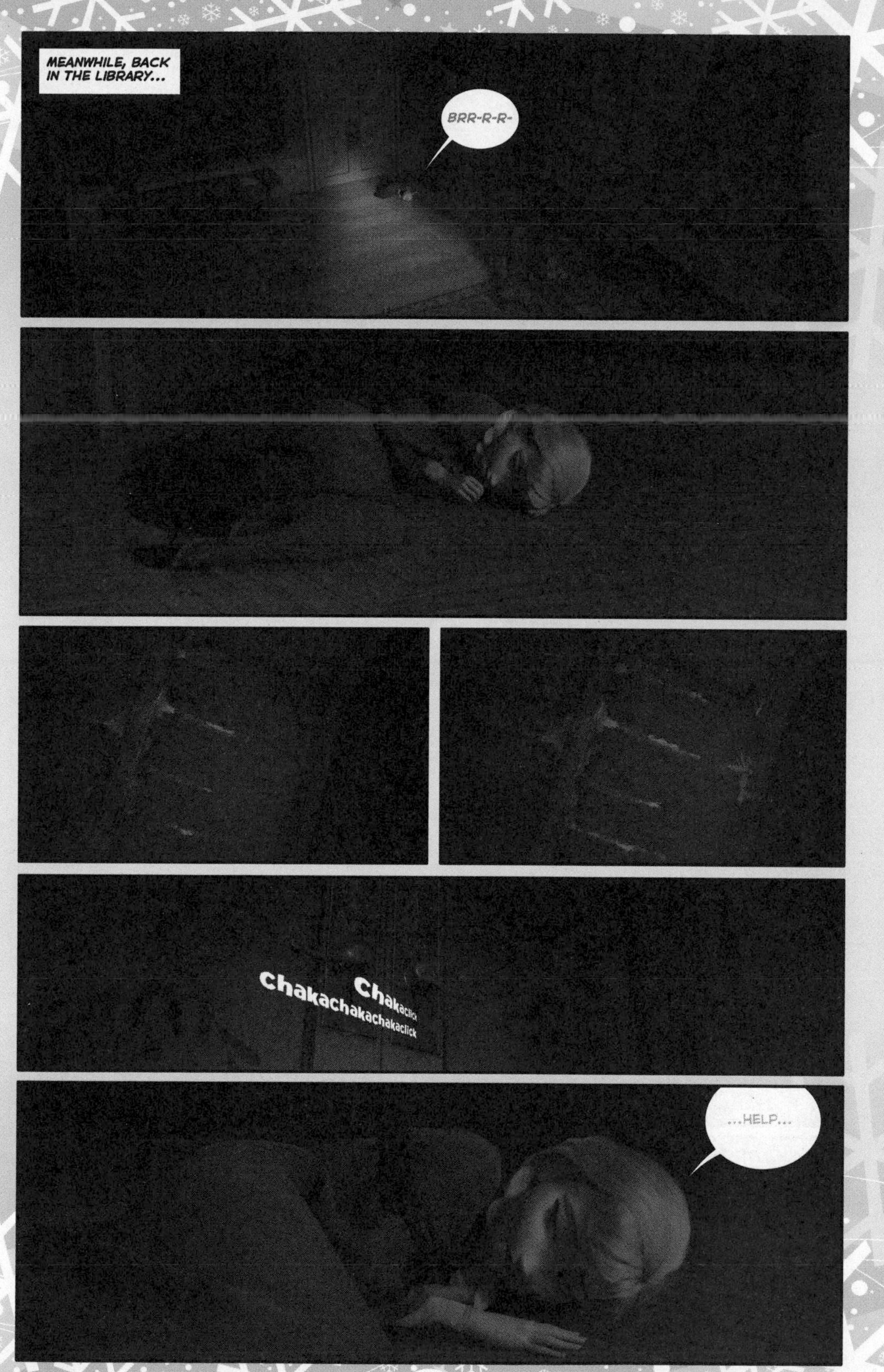
MEANWHILE, BACK IN THE LIBRARY...
BRR-R-R-
Chakaclick
Chakachakachakaclick
...HELP...

Clak
creeeak
HEEHEEHEH-
HAH!
GASP -
ANNA!
OH, NO!

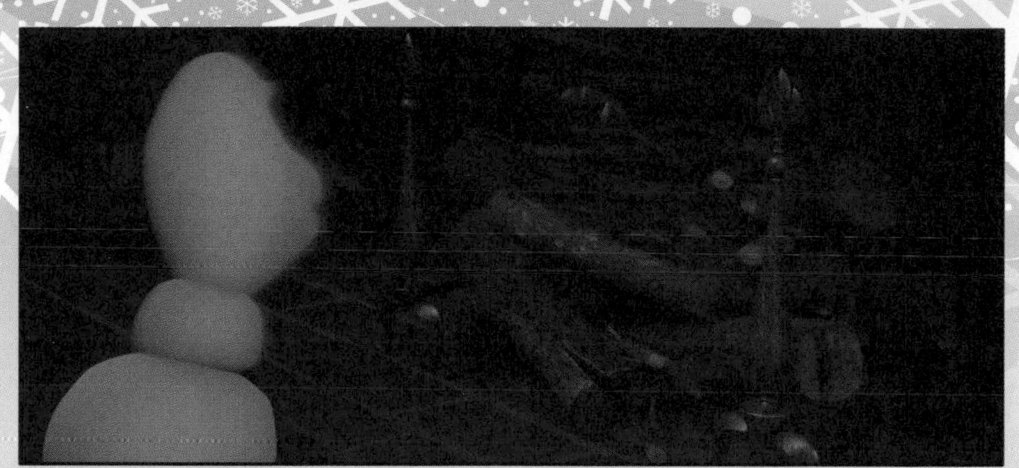

EEP!

AHH, THERE WE GO.

SKRITCH

O-OLAF?

WOOOOW.

OLAF, GET AWAY FROM THERE!

SO THIS IS HEAT. I LOVE IT.

OH! BUT DON'T TOUCH IT!

COME ON -- LET'S GET YOU WARMED UP.

SO, WHERE'S HANS? WHAT HAPPENED TO YOUR KISS?
I WAS WRONG ABOUT HIM. IT WASN'T TRUE LOVE.
BUT WE RAN ALL THE WAY HERE!
PLEASE, OLAF. YOU C-CAN'T STAY HERE. YOU'LL MELT.
I AM NOT LEAVING HERE UNTIL WE FIND SOME OTHER ACT OF TRUE LOVE TO SAVE YOU.
...DO YOU HAPPEN TO HAVE ANY IDEAS?
I DON'T EVEN KNOW WHAT LOVE IS.

THAT'S OKAY, I DO!
LOVE IS... PUTTING SOMEONE ELSE'S NEEDS BEFORE YOURS.
LIKE, Y'KNOW, HOW KRISTOFF BROUGHT YOU BACK HERE TO HANS AND LEFT YOU FOREVER.

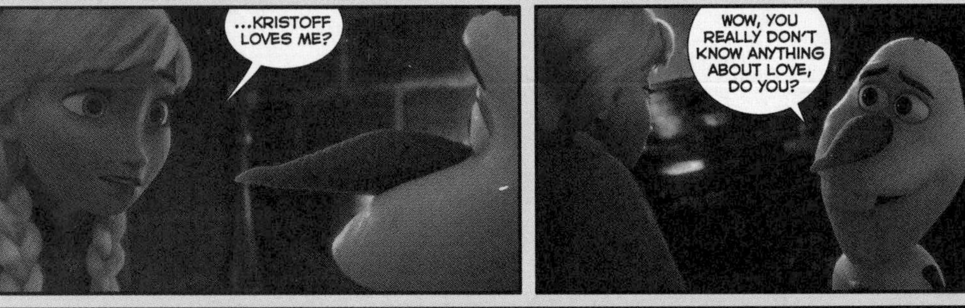
...KRISTOFF LOVES ME?
WOW, YOU REALLY DON'T KNOW ANYTHING ABOUT LOVE, DO YOU?

OLAF, YOU'RE MELTING!

SOME PEOPLE ARE WORTH MELTING FOR...

...BUT MAYBE NOT THIS SECOND!

KRAK

DON'T WORRY, I'VE GOT IT!

NFF

WE'RE GONNA GET THROUGH--

OH, WAIT.

HANG ON, I'M GETTING SOMETHING...

KRAK

CRUNCH

AH! IT'S KRISTOFF AND SVEN!

THEY'RE COMING BACK THIS WAY!

THEY-THEY ARE?

WOW, HE'S REALLY MOVING FAST. I GUESS I WAS WRONG.

I GUESS KRISTOFF DOESN'T LOVE YOU ENOUGH TO LEAVE YOU BEHIND.

HELP ME UP, OLAF! PLEASE!

NO-NO-NO-NO-NO!

STAY BY THE FIRE AND KEEP WARM!

I NEED TO GET TO KRISTOFF.
WHY?

OH! OH I KNOW WHY!

THERE'S YOUR ACT OF TRUE LOVE RIGHT THERE, RIDING ACROSS THE FJORDS LIKE A VALIANT, PUNGENT REINDEER KING! COME ON!

OH, GULP!
CRAKCRACK
CRAKCRACK

LOOK OUT!

THIS WAY!
UH!
CRAKCRA
CRAKCRACK

UH... NO, BACK THAT WAY!

CRAKCRACK

WE'RE TRAPPED!

CRAKCRACK
CRAKCRACK

CRAKCRACK
CRAKCRACK
CRAKCRACK

CRAKCRACK

OH--!

WHOAH!
CRAK-SHH

THE STORM IS OUT OF CONTROL!

SLIDE, ANNA!

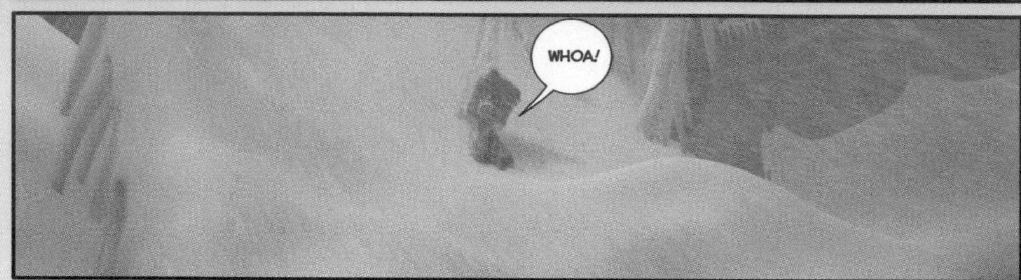
WHOA!

WUBBA-
BUBBA-WUBBA-
WHOA!

WE
MADE
IT!

GO, GO,
GO, GO
GO!

KRISTOFF RACES ONTO THE FROZEN FJORDS, TOWARDS ANNA...

...NOT KNOWING THAT, SOMEWHERE IN THE APPROACHING WINDSTORM, SHE'S LOOKING FOR HIM.

BRR--

C'MON, BUDDY - FASTER!
BRAAW!

KRISTOFF...?

KRISTOFF!

OH!
WHOA-
WHOA--

KEEP GOING!

KRISTOFF!

ANNA YELLS, BUT KRISTOFF CAN'T HEAR HER ON THE OTHER SIDE OF THE GROUNDED SHIP...

C'MON!

KRISTOFF--
CRAKCRACK
CRAKCRACK

CRAKCRACK
CRAKCRACK

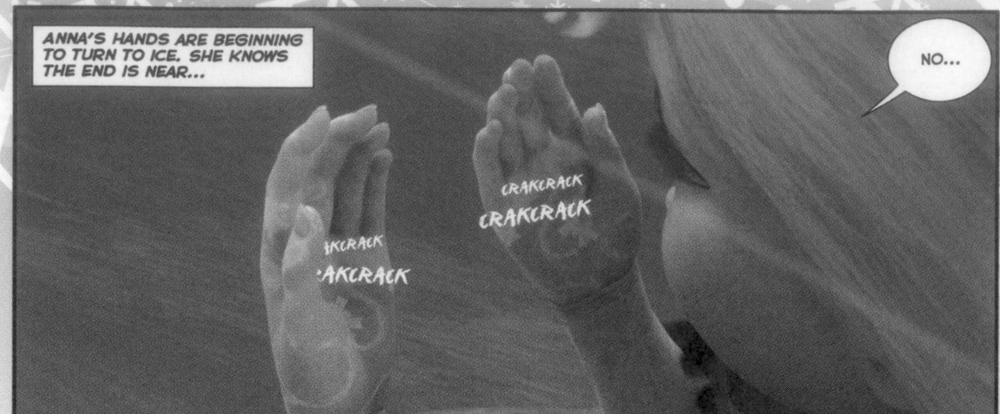
ANNA'S HANDS ARE BEGINNING TO TURN TO ICE. SHE KNOWS THE END IS NEAR...
NO...
CRAKCRACK
CRAKCRACK

HER HEART IS BEGINNING TO FREEZE.

THE SHIP --

IT'S COMING APART!

GO!

YOU CAN DO IT, SVEN!

C'MON, BUDDY...

CRRR-CRRRR

WHOA---

SNERRT!

WHA-
HOAAA!!!

SVEN?

SVEN!!

SNRRRT

BRRAAAW!

WHEW.
GOOD BOY.

I'LL COME BACK FOR YOU, SVEN! STAY PUT!

OH...

K-KRISTOFF--?

K-KRISTOFF--?
GASP!

ANNA!

NO!

ELSA!
YOU CAN'T RUN FROM THIS!

JUST - - JUST TAKE CARE OF MY SISTER!

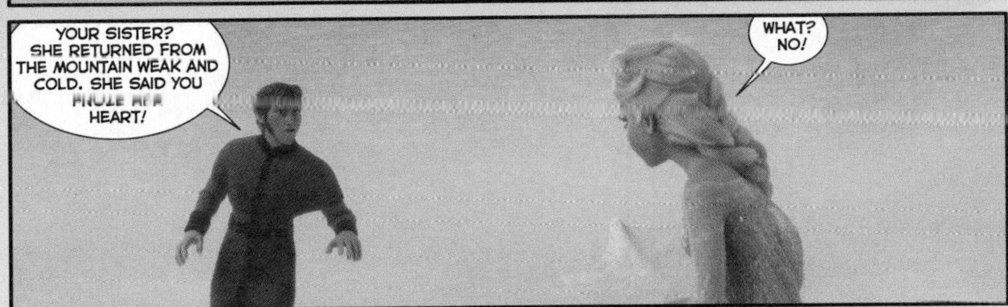
YOUR SISTER? SHE RETURNED FROM THE MOUNTAIN WEAK AND COLD. SHE SAID YOU
HEART!
WHAT? NO!

I TRIED TO SAVE HER, BUT IT WAS TOO LATE. HER SKIN WAS ICE, HER HAIR TURNED WHITE...

YOUR SISTER IS DEAD...

...BECAUSE OF YOU.

ELSA IS STUNNED. THE SHOCK OF ANNA'S DEATH CAUSES THE SWIRLING STORM TO FREEZE, SNOWFLAKES SUSPENDED IN MID-AIR, TRAPPED IN GRIEF.

...KRISTOFF...

ANNA!

THE SOUND OF A SWORD BEING DRAWN CAUSES ANNA'S HEAD TO TURN.
SHIIIIING

ANNA CAN FEEL HER HEART SLOWING, TURNING TO ICE.
SHE COULD RUN TO KRISTOFF AND BE SAVED BY A TRUE LOVE'S KISS...

...OR SHE COULD HELP HER SISTER. THERE'S NOT TIME TO DO BOTH.

...ANNA?

NO!

IT IS THE LAST THING ANNA DOES...
CRAKCRACK

...BEFORE THE REST OF HER BODY TRANSFORMS INTO ICE.
CRAKCRACKKKK

SHRKRAAAKKLLKRAK

WHAT?!?

HANS SHOULD HAVE EASILY CUT THROUGH THE ICE STATUE ANNA HAD BECOME...
...BUT THE SAME MAGIC THAT HAS FROZEN HER INSTEAD SHATTERS HIS BLADE... AND SENDS HIM FLYING.

CRAKCRACKRRR

ANNA?

ANNA?

NO!
SNIFF

OH, NO
NO NO--!

ANNA?

...OH.

WITH THE STORM FROZEN IN PLACE, EVERYONE HAD A CLEAR VIEW OF WHAT HAD HAPPENED.

HOW HANS HAD LIED ABOUT ANNA...

...AND HOW ANNA HAD HEROICALLY SAVED HER SISTER.

AND THEN, WHILE QUEEN ELSA SOBBED, THEY SAW SOMETHING ELSE...

KRICKLE

KRICKLE

GASP

SNRTT?

KRICKLEKRI
CKLEKRICK

...THEY SAW THE POWER OF TRUE LOVE.
OH!

ANNA?

ANNA!

OH, ELSA!

YOU SACRIFICED YOURSELF... FOR ME?

I LOVE YOU.

AH! AN ACT OF TRUE LOVE WILL THAW A FROZEN HEART!

LOVE WILL THAW.

LOVE, OF COURSE!
ELSA?

LOVE!

SNRRTT?

THE FROZEN FJORD THAWS.

OH!
LOOK!

ICED OVER FOUNTAINS SPRING BACK TO LIFE.

THE SNOW LIFTS...

...SWEEPING UP ALL OF THE ICE ELSA HAD CREATED.

FLOWERS BLOOM.
HEE HEE!

THE SKY CLEARS.

THE SNOW SWIRLS...

...AND RISES...

...AND DISAPPEARS.

SHE HAS FINALLY
SOLVED THE PUZZLE.

FREE OF THE FEARS OF HER CHILDHOOD, THE KEY TO CONTROLLING HER POWER WAS LOVE.

ANNA'S LOVE SHOWED HER THE WAY.

OH!

I KNEW YOU COULD DO IT!

HANDS DOWN, THIS IS THE BEST DAY OF MY LIFE...

...AND QUITE POSSIBLY THE LAST.

OH, OLAF...
FWHOOSH-

HANG ON, LITTLE GUY.

OH! OH!
OH!

MY OWN
PERSONAL
FLURRY!
GIGGLE

COUGH!

UNGH...
OW...

YOU...
AH-AH-AH!

AHEM.

ANNA?
BUT SHE FROZE YOUR HEART!

THE ONLY FROZEN HEART AROUND HERE --

-- IS YOURS.
WHAM
OW--

YAAAAAAHH--
SPLURRSHH

HAHAHAHA!
FANTASTIQUE!
HAHAHAHA!

BRRAAAW.

A FEW DAYS LATER...
I WILL RETURN THIS SCOUNDREL, HANS, TO HIS COUNTRY.

WE WILL SEE WHAT HIS TWELVE BIG BROTHERS THINK OF HIS BEHAVIOR.

ARENDELLE THANKS YOU, MY LORD.

THIS IS UNACCEPTABLE. I AM INNOCENT. I'M A VICTIM OF FEAR, I'VE BEEN TRAUMATIZED.

OW! MY NECK HURTS! IS THERE A DOCTOR I COULD...
...NO?

AND I DEMAND TO SEE THE QUEEN!
OH, I HAVE A MESSAGE FROM THE QUEEN.

ARENDELLE WILL HENCEFORTH AND FOREVER NO LONGER DO BUSINESS OF ANY SORT WITH WEASELTOWN.

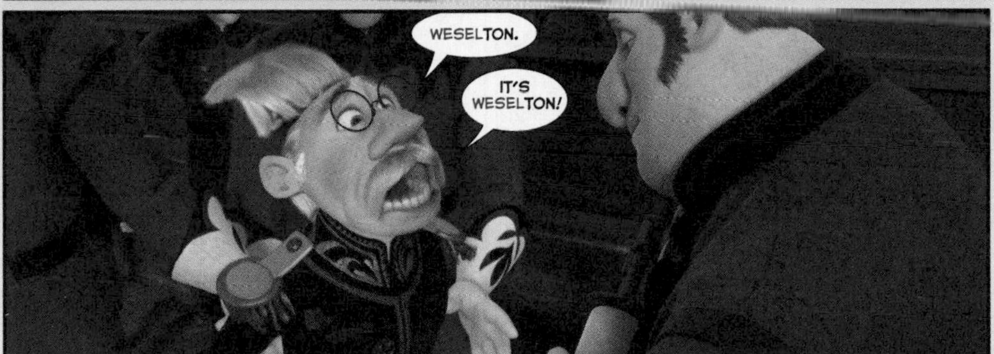
WESELTON.
IT'S WESELTON!

MEANWHILE...
COME ON! C'MON, C'MON, C'MON!
OKAY, OKAY, HERE I COME--

WHUNG
OW! --POLE.

OOPS. SORRY.

OKAY!
OKAY, WE ARE HERE!

OH!

SQUEE!

I OWE YOU A SLED!

ARE YOU SERIOUS?
EEE! YES! AND IT'S THE LATEST MODEL!
NO, I CAN'T ACCEPT THIS--!

YOU HAVE TO. NO RETURNS. NO EXCHANGES. QUEEN'S ORDERS.

SNRRT.

SHE'S NAMED YOU THE OFFICIAL ARENDELLE ICE MASTER AND DELIVERER.

IT EVEN HAS A CUP HOLDER!
--DO YOU LIKE IT?
LIKE IT? I LOVE IT! I COULD KISS YOU!

...I COULD. I MEAN I'D LIKE TO. I'D... MAY I? WE ME....I MEAN, MAY WE?

WAIT,
WHAT?

SMACK

WE MAY.

SUMMER!
GIGGLE

OH, HELLO!
SNIFFFFF AHHH...

EYAAAH-AH-AH--

AH-CHOO!

GASP!

SHLURP!
EEEK!

AW.

PLOP
BRAAAW!

HYUK!

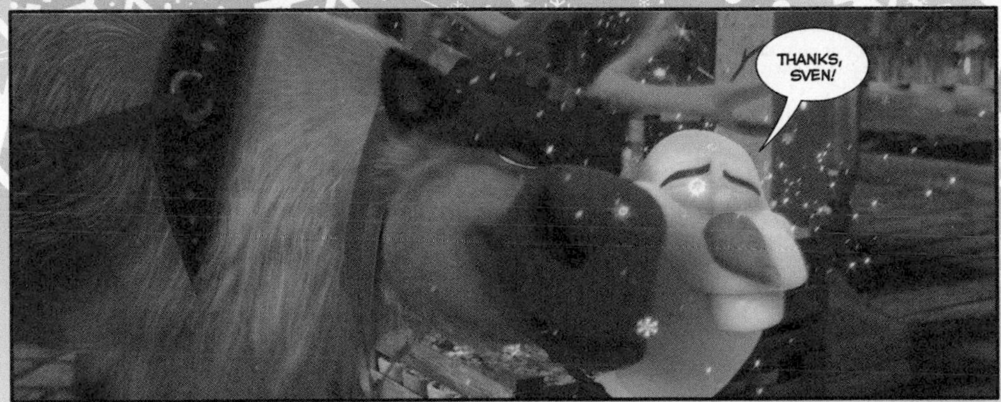
THANKS, SVEN!

ARE YOU READY?

CLAP CLAP CLAP CLAP CLAP CLAP

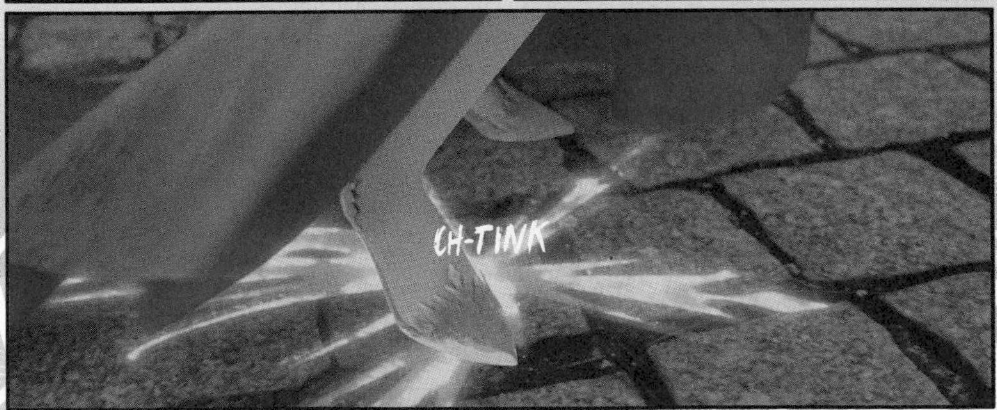
CH-TINK

ELSA LETS LOOSE HER MAGIC AGAIN, IN FULL CONTROL, AND WITH NO FEAR...

WOO!
WOO!

HER PEOPLE HAVE ACCEPTED HER, NOT AS A QUEEN WITH A CURSE --
CRAKCRACK
CRAKCRACK

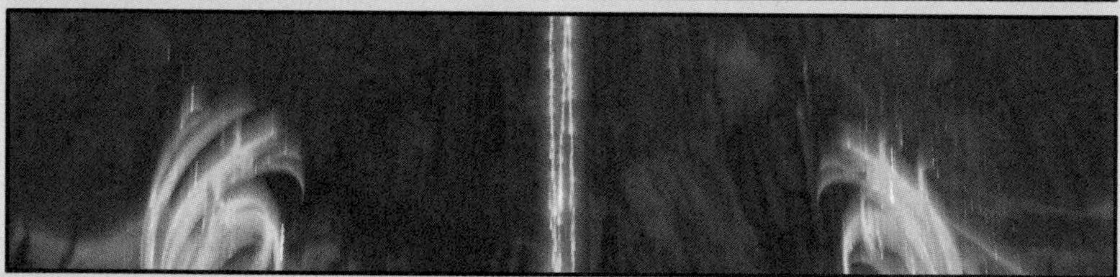

-- BUT A QUEEN WITH A WONDERFUL GIFT.

HAHA!

WHEE!

WHOAH-
OOOP.

I LIKE
THE OPEN
GATES.

WE ARE NEVER CLOSING THEM AGAIN.

FWAASH

OH, ELSA, THEY'RE BEAUTIFUL.

BUT YOU KNOW I DON'T SKA--

COME ON! DO IT!

LOOK OUT! REINDEER COMIN' THROUGH!

HA-HAH!
HEY, GUYS!

THAT'S RIGHT, ANNA-GLIDE AND PIVOT.

GLIDE AND PIVOT...

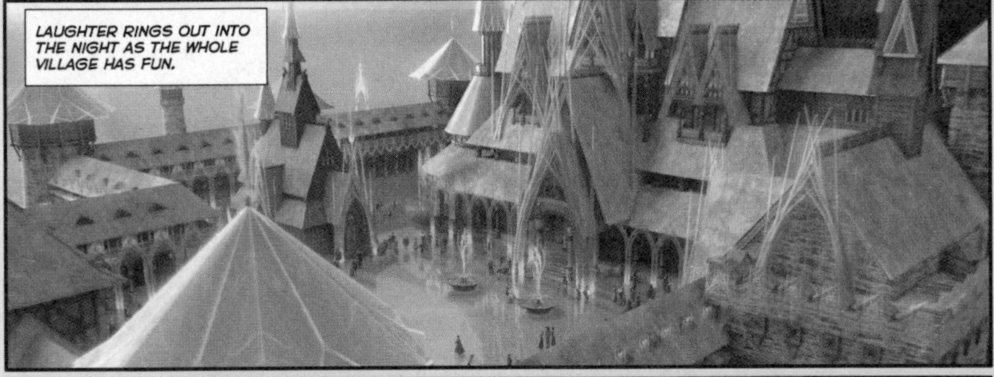
LAUGHTER RINGS OUT INTO THE NIGHT AS THE WHOLE VILLAGE HAS FUN.

AND ALL IS RIGHT IN ARENDELLE.
THE END.

STORY INSPIRED BY
"THE SNOW QUEEN"
BY HANS CHRISTIAN ANDERSEN

STORY BY
CHRIS BUCK
JENNIFER LEE
SHANE MORRIS

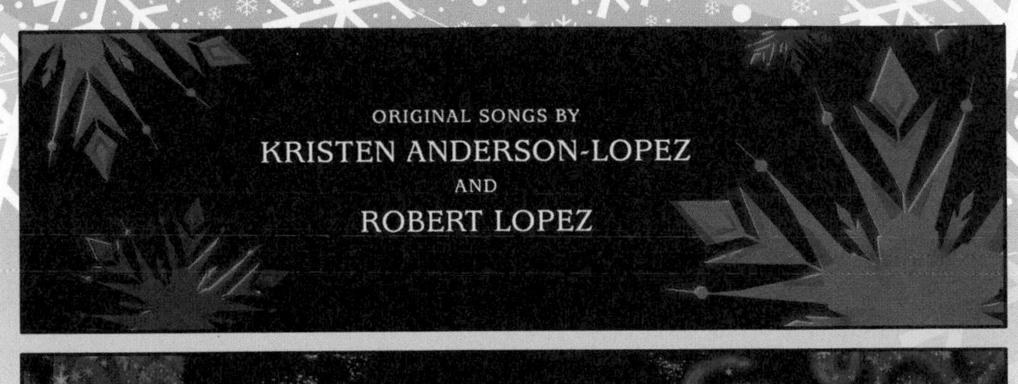

ORIGINAL SONGS BY
KRISTEN ANDERSON-LOPEZ
AND
ROBERT LOPEZ

ORIGINAL SCORE COMPOSED BY
CHRISTOPHE BECK

ASSOCIATE PRODUCER
AIMEE SCRIBNER

EDITOR
JEFF DRAHEIM

VISUAL EFFECTS SUPERVISOR
STEVE GOLDBERG

ART DIRECTOR
MICHAEL GIAIMO

ASSISTANT ART DIRECTOR
LISA KEENE

PRODUCTION DESIGNER
DAVID WOMERSLEY

CHARACTER DESIGN SUPERVISOR
BILL SCHWAB

PRODUCTION MANAGER
NICOLE P. HEARON

HEAD OF STORY
PAUL BRIGGS

HEAD OF ANIMATION
LINO Di SALVO

DIRECTOR OF CINEMATOGRAPHY, LAYOUT
SCOTT BEATTIE

DIRECTOR OF CINEMATOGRAPHY, LIGHTING
MOHIT KALLIANPUR

TECHNICAL SUPERVISOR
MARK HAMMEL

CHARACTER CG SUPERVISOR
FRANK HANNER

MODELING SUPERVISOR, CHARACTERS
CHAD STUBBLEFIELD

MODELING SUPERVISOR, ENVIRONMENTS
JON KIM KRUMMEL II

LOOK SUPERVISOR, CHARACTERS
MICHELLE LEE ROBINSON

LOOK SUPERVISOR, ENVIRONMENTS
HANS-JOERG E. KEIM

CHARACTER TD SUPERVISOR, SIMULATION
KEITH WILSON

CHARACTER TD SUPERVISORS, RIGGING
CARLOS CABRAL
GREGORY SMITH

TECHNICAL ANIMATION SUPERVISOR
MARK EMPEY

EFFECTS SUPERVISORS
DALE MAYEDA
MARLON WEST

STEREOSCOPIC SUPERVISOR
KATIE A. FICO

ANIMATION SUPERVISORS
REBECCA WILSON BRESEE
HYRUM VIRL OSMOND
MALCON B. PIERCE III
TONY SMEED
WAYNE UNTEN
LIGHTING SUPERVISORS
ALESSANDRO JACOMINI
HANS-JOERG E. KEIM
RICHARD E. LEHMANN
JASON MacLEOD
ROBERT L. MILES
AMOL SATHE
JOSH STAUB
ASSOCIATE TECHNICAL SUPERVISORS
THADDEUS P. MILLER
RICKY RIECKENBERG
EXECUTIVE MUSIC PRODUCER
CHRIS MONTAN
MUSIC SUPERVISOR
TOM MacDOUGALL
POST PRODUCTION EXECUTIVE
BÉRÉNICE ROBINSON
SUPERVISING SOUND EDITOR/
SOUND DESIGNER
ODIN BENITEZ

Casting by
JAMIE SPARER ROBERTS, CSA

CAST

Anna KRISTEN BELL
Elsa IDINA MENZEL
Kristoff JONATHAN GROFF
Olaf JOSH GAD
Hans SANTINO FONTANA
Duke ALAN TUDYK
Pabbie/Grandpa CIARÁN HINDS
Oaken CHRIS WILLIAMS
Kai STEPHEN JOHN ANDERSON
Bulda MAIA WILSON
Gerda EDIE McCLURG
Bishop ROBERT PINE
King MAURICE LaMARCHE
Young Anna LIVVY STUBENRAUCH
Young Elsa EVA BELLA
Teen Elsa SPENCER GANUS
Spanish Dignitary JESSE CORTI
German Dignitary JEFFREY MARCUS
Irish Dignitary TUCKER GILMORE

Additional Voices
AVA ACRES STEPHEN APOSTOLINA
ANNALEIGH ASHFORD KIRK BAILY
JENICA BERGERE DAVE BOAT
PAUL BRIGGS TYREE BROWN
WOODY BUCK JUNE CHRISTOPHER
LEWIS CLEALE WENDY CUTLER
TERRI DOUGLAS EDDIE FRIERSON
JEAN GILPIN JACKIE GONNEAU
NICHOLAS GUEST BRIDGET HOFFMAN
NICK JAMESON DANIEL KAZ
JOHN LAVELLE JENNIFER LEE
PAT LENTZ ANNIE LOPEZ
KATIE LOWES MONA MARSHALL
DARA McGARRY SCOTT MENVILLE
ADAM OVERETT PAUL PAPE
COURTNEY PELDON JENNIFER PERRY
RAYMOND S. PERSI JEAN-MICHEL RICHAUD
LYNWOOD ROBINSON CARTER SAND
JADON SAND KATIE SILVERMAN
PEPPER SWEENEY FRED TATASCIORE

Casting Associate CYMBRE WALK

Production Finance Lead
BELINDA M. HSU

STORY

Production Supervisor JESSICA JULIUS

Story Artists
CLIO CHIANG NORMAND LEMAY
STEVEN MARKOWSKI NICOLE MITCHELL
RAYMOND S. PERSI JEFFREY RESOLME RANJO
JOHN RIPA MARC SMITH
FAWN VEERASUNTHORN CHRIS WILLIAMS

Additional Story Artists
STEPHEN ANDERSON KELLY ASBURY
DON DOUGHERTY TOM ELLERY
NATHAN GRENO KEVIN HARKEY
KENDELLE HOYER BARRY JOHNSON
MARK KENNEDY JEREMY SPEARS
CHRIS URE DEAN WELLINS

Additional Story by KRISTEN ANDERSON-LOPEZ
Story Apprentice JIHYUN PARK
Production Assistants ASHLEY READ
ELISE M. L. SCANLAN

EDITORIAL

Production Supervisor HEATHER BLODGET
First Assistant Editors ANTHONY DURAZZO
ERIC WHITFIELD
Second Assistant Editor BRIAN MILLMAN
Dialogue Reader HERMANN H. SCHMIDT
Additional Editorial Support RICK HAMMEL
DANYA JOSEPH
KAREN WHITE
Production Coordinator LEAH LATHAM
Production Assistant MICHELLE McMILLAN

VISUAL DEVELOPMENT

Production Supervisor JAMES E. HASMAN

Visual Development Artists
JAMES A. FINCH JIM FINN
MAC GEORGE JEAN GILLMORE
CLAIRE KEANE LISA KEENE
JIN KIM SHIYOON KIM
BRITTNEY LEE HYUN-MIN LEE
MINKYU LEE CORY LOFTIS
DAN LUND BILL PERKINS
JEAN-CHRISTOPHE POULAIN DOUG WALKER
DAVID WOMERSLEY VICTORIA YING

Additional Visual Development
SARAH AIRRIESS SUNNY APINCHAPONG
RUBEN A. AQUINO DALE L. BAER
ADAM DYKSTRA BRIAN FERGUSON
ANDY HARKNESS RANDY HAYCOCK
MARK HENN JULIA KALANTAROVA
ALEX KUPERSHMIDT KEVIN NELSON
BRUCE W. SMITH FRANS VISCHER
LARRY WU

ASSET PRODUCTION

Production Supervisor, Characters NATHAN CURTIS
Production Supervisor, Environments JAMES E. HASMAN

Character TDs, Rigging
JESUS CANAL IKER J. de los MOZOS
JOY JOHNSON SCOTT PETERS
NICKLAS PUETZ MATT SCHILLER
MATT STEELE DAVID J. SUROVIEC

Character TDs, Simulation
AARON ADAMS JENNIFER R. DOWNS
ERIK EULEN AVNEET KAUR
HUBERT LEO JEFF MacNEILL
CLAUDIA CHUNG SANII TIMMY TOMPKINS
MARC THYNG MARY TWOHIG
XINMIN ZHAO

Modelers
SHAUN ABSHER CHRISTOPHER ANDERSON
VIRGILIO JOHN AQUINO NADJA BONACINA
CHARLES CUNNINGHAM-SCOTT STEFANO DUBAY
DYLAN EKREN BRIEN HINDMAN
KEVIN HUDSON HIROKI ITOKAZU
JACKY KE JIANG SUZAN KIM
LUIS LABRADOR BRANDON LAWLESS
IRENE MATAR CHRIS PATRICK O'CONNELL
FLORIAN PERRET ERIC PROVAN
EDWARD E. ROBBINS III SAMY SEGURA
JUAN SOLIS GARCÍA RYAN TOTTLE
ALENA WOOTEN TOTTLE

[illegible] [illegible] CASTRO
Production Assistants, Characters ALLISON MARTIN
KIT TURLEY
Production Assistant, Environments JASMINE GONZALEZ

LOOK DEVELOPMENT

Production Supervisor MIKE HUANG
Pre-Production Supervisor CHUCK TAPPAN
Pre-Production Look Supervisor RYAN DUNCAN
Look Lead LANCE SUMMERS

Look Development Artists
ALEXANDER ALVARADO JOAN ANASTAS
AUDREY BAGLEY SARA VIRGINIA CEMBALISTY
TRACY LEE CHURCH CHARLES COLLADAY
PAULA GOLDSTEIN JOHN HUIKKU
DAVID WILKES KERSEY CHELSEA LAVERTU
MIA LEE KONRAD LIGHTNER
VICKY YUTZU LIN JARED REISWEBER
MITCHELL SNARY PAMELA SPERTUS
SHERI WONG

Matte Painter JANG LEE

Look Development Apprentices
RAMYA CHIDANAND NIKKI MULL JOSE LUIS "WEECHO" VELASQUEZ

Look Development TDs
STELLA HSIN-HUEI CHENG MARC COOPER PATRICK DALTON
TAL LANCASTER LEWIS N. SIEGEL

Production Coordinator CAITLIN PEAK COONS

LAYOUT

Production Supervisor TUCKER GILMORE
Layout Lead/Camera Polish CORY ROCCO FLORIMONTE

Layout Artists
JOAQUIN BALDWIN ALLEN BLAISDELL
DANIEL HU KEVIN LEE
TERRY MOEWS RICK MOORE
MERRICK RUSTIA MATSUNE SUZUKI
KENDRA VANDER VLIET DAVID WAINSTAIN
DOUG WALKER NATHAN DETROIT WARNER

Layout Apprentices TYLER KUPFERER
MATT SULLIVAN
Layout Trainee SCOTT ARMSTRONG
Layout Finaling Artists CELESTE JOANETTE
TAMARA ALEJANDRA FARALLA KERSAVAGE
MICHAEL TALARICO
Layout TDs MIKE HARRIS
JEFF SADLER
SHWETA VISWANATHAN
Production Coordinator ALBERT V. RAMIREZ
Production Assistant ALLISON MARTIN

ANIMATION

Production Supervisor ANGELA FRANCES D'ANNA
Lead 2D Animator MARK HENN

Animators
ALBERTO ABRIL VALENTIN AMADOR DIAZ
DOUG BENNETT JOEY BROWN
DARRIN BUTTERS ANDREW CHESWORTH
YOUNGJAE CHOI CHRISTOPHER CORDINGLEY
STEVE CUNNINGHAM AMANDA DAGUE
PATRICK DANAHER RENATO DOS ANJOS
JEFFREY ENGEL CHADD FERRON
JASON FIGLIOZZI MICHAEL FRANCESCHI
DEREK FRIESENBORG MINOR JOSE GAYTAN
RYAN GONG STEVEN PIERRE GORDON
ADAM GREEN JENNIFER HAGER
RYAN HOBBIEBRUNKEN ROBERT HUTH
DARRELL JOHNSON MACK KABLAN
JOHN KAHRS MIYUKI KANNO LONG
CLAY KAYTIS MÍCHEÁL KIELY
BERT KLEIN MICHAEL KLIM
DANIEL JAMES KLUG MATT KUMMER
ANDREW LAWSON HYUN-MIN LEE
KIRA LEHTOMAKI KEVIN MacLEAN
STEPHANE MANGIN KELLY McCLANAHAN
BRIAN F. MENZ MATTHEW MEYER
MARK MITCHELL MARLON NOWE
DANIEL MARTÍN PEIXE BOBBY PONTILLAS
NICOLAS PROTHAIS MITJA RABAR
JOEL REID BURKE ROANE
BRIAN SCOTT CHAD SELLERS
BENSON SHUM JUSTIN SKLAR
AMY LAWSON SMEED BILL TESSIER
GEOFF WHEELER MARK A. WILLIAMS
JOHN WONG KATHY ZIELINSKI

Animating Assistants

RIANNON DELANOY MARAT DAVLETSHIN
MARIO FURMANCZYK DANIEL GONZALES III
SVETLA RADIVOEVA RASTKO STEFANOVIC
MICHAEL WOODSIDE

Animation Apprentices

FRANK E. ABNEY III ANDREW ATTEBERRY
TONY CHAU TRENT CORREY
JORGE GARCIA JORGE E. RUIZ C.
JUSTIN WEBER

Animation TDs FABRICE CEUGNIET
CHRISTOPHER OTTO GALLAGHER
REBECCA VALLERA-THOMPSON
Production Coordinators LAURA M. MEREDITH
KIT TURLEY
Production Assistant JESSICA "JAC" CHEN

TECHNICAL ANIMATION

Production Supervisor KRISTIN LEIGH YADAMEC

Technical Animation Artists

ARTURO AGUILAR VIRGILIO JOHN AQUINO
KATHLEEN M. BAILEY BRET BAYS
COREY BOLWYN NICHOLAS BURKARD
AARON CAMPBELL JESUS CANAL
GLEN CLAYBROOK CASEY DAME
ERIK EULEN CHRISTOPHER EVART
JAY GAMBELL ROSE IBIAMA
ANDREW JENNINGS JOY JOHNSON
WILLIAM D. KASTAK SI-HYUNG KIM
ADAM REED LEVY MAIA NEUBIG
NAVIN MARTIN PINTO BRYAN POON
LUIS SAN JUAN PALLARES MICHAEL W. STIEBER
DAVID J. SUROVIEC JOHN TRUONG
RICHARD VAN CLEAVE JR. ERIC WARREN
ZACK WEILER WALTER YODER

Production Coordinator BRANDON HOLMES
Production Assistant AUSTIN SALMI

CROWD ANIMATION

Production Supervisor KRISTIN LEIGH YADAMEC
Crowd Lead MOE EL-ALI
Crowd Artists ERIN J. ELLIOTT
JOHN MURRAH
TUAN NGUYEN
Additional Crowd Artist YASSER HAMED
Production Coordinator BRANDON HOLMES
Production Assistant AUSTIN SALMI

EFFECTS

Production Supervisor LESLEY ADDARIO BENTIVEGNA
Effects Designers IAN J. COONY
DAN LUND

Effects Animators

MIR ALI JUSTIN ANDREWS
ERIC W. ARAUJO BOB BENNETT
BRETT BOGGS MARC BRYANT
DONG JOO BYUN CHRIS CARIGNAN
MICHAEL CHAPMAN ERIC DANIELS
JESSE ERICKSON BENJAMIN FISKE
BEN FROST CHRISTOPHER HENDRYX
DAVID HUTCHINS JOHN HUGHES
SAM KLOCK JOHN KOSNIK
JAMES DeV. MANSFIELD TIM MOLINDER
DAN NAULIN MIKE NAVARRO
HENDRIK PANZ BLAIR PIERPONT
DAVE RAND BRIAN SILVA
KEE NAM SUONG ZUBIN WADIA
THOMAS WICKES BRUCE WRIGHT
JAE HYUN YOO XIAO ZHANG

Effects TDs TONY CHAI
VIJOY GADDIPATI
NEELIMA KARANAM
Effects Apprentices SHAN DUAN
RATTANIN SIRINARUEMARN
Additional Effects LAWRENCE CHAI
ALEXEY DMITRIEVICH STOMAKHIN
Production Coordinator MELISSA GENOSHE
Production Assistant MATT SCHIAVONE

LIGHTING

Production Supervisor SHERI PATTERSON

Lighting Artists

JOAN ANASTAS SALVADOR ARDITTI
JASON BARLOW JEFFREY BENEDICT
KEN BRAIN COREY BUTLER
ONNY CARR JEFF CHUNG
GREGORY CULP CHERYL DAVIS
RYAN DeYOUNG JUSTIN DOBIES
KAORI DOI SHANT ERGENIAN
JOSH FRY ALEX GARCIA
LOGAN GLOOR PAULA GOLDSTEIN
RICHARD GOUGE BENJAMIN MIN HUANG
ADRIAN ILER KATHERINE IPJIAN
IVA ITCHEVSKA-BRAIN ARTHUR JEPPE
JONGO BLAINE KENNISON
HOLLY KIM-ANGEL MacDUFF KNOX
KEVIN KONEVAL DAN KRUSE
GINA LAWES ROGER LEE
DAN LEVY BENJAMIN LISHKA
VINA KAO MAHONEY JONATHAN FLETCHER MOORE
CRISTIAN G. MORAS CHRIS NABHOLZ
DEREK NELSON JAMES NEWLAND
ALEX NIJMEH STEPHEN NULL
EILEEN O'NEILL JORGE OBREGON
AMY PFAFFINGER ELLEN POON
ALAN PRECOURT WINSTON QUITASOL
KATIE REIHMAN DANIEL RICE
OLUN RILEY FRANK A. SABIA JR.
WALLY SCHAAB ROBERT SHOWALTER
MARK SIEGEL KA YAW TAN
FATEMA TARZI EMILY TSE
ELIZABETH WILLY FARID YAZAMI
JENNIFER YU NASHEET ZAMAN
DIANA J. ZENG

SOFTWARE INFRASTRUCTURE

Technology Manager KEVIN GAMBREL

MARTY ALCHIN
NEIL P. BARBER
DALE BECK
JORDI CARRILLO BOSCH
MARK R. CARLSON
KYLE D. HAYES
PAUL HILDEBRANDT
HIDE A. HIRASE
MICHAEL D. KLIEWER
STEFAN LUKA
CHRISTOPHER D. MIHALY
G. KEVIN MORGAN
JOHN ROBERT PERRY
WENDY M. TAM
ROY TURNER

SYSTEMS ENGINEERING

Technology Manager RONALD L. JOHNSON
Principal Engineers SCOTT BURRIS
MARC JORDAN
DOUG WHITE
CURTIS ZINZILIETA

RICHARD BOMBERGER
STEVEN C. CARPENTER
KEVIN C. CONSTANTINE
TOM CORRIGAN
THOMAS GREER
JAY HILLIARD
DANNY JEWELL
NAVNEIL KUMAR
JAMES MacBURNEY
MICHAEL A. McCLURE
STUART McDOUGAL
GREG NEAGLE
KIMBERLY M. RIOS
STEVEN SEED
ZACHARY STOKES
PAUL TAKAHASHI
ROSIE WACHA
MATT WATSON
GRAHAM B. WHITTED IV

SYSTEMS MOBILE DEVELOPMENT

Technology Manager MATTHEW SCHNITTKER

DIANA STONE TRUONG VO

SYSTEMS OPERATIONS

Technology Manager JAMES COLBY BETTE

VINCE D'AMORE CARLOS "CHARLIE" ESTIANDAN
ERIC N. GARCIA MATTHEW GOODMAN
ALAN A. PATEL DEREK E. WILSON

TECHNICAL SUPPORT

Technology Manager SHANNON R. HOWARD

NATALIE ACOSTA PETER LEE CHUN
MICHAEL DOBSON MICHAEL M. FUKUMOTO
JOSH PADILLA JOHN READICK
GRACE H. SHIRADO MICHAEL WEISSMAN

Technology Assistant Manager DAYNA B. MELTZER
Sr. Graphic Designer JAMES LAVRAKAS
Technology Coordinator DAWN HALLORAN
Sr. Research Scientist RASMUS TAMSTORF

THE STAFF OF WALT DISNEY ANIMATION STUDIOS

Studio Leadership

JOHN LASSETER ED CATMULL
ANDREW MILLSTEIN GREG COLEMAN
ROY CONLI PETER DEL VECHO
ANDY HENDRICKSON ALAN KEITH
ANN LE CAM JOHN I. McGUIRE
DOROTHY McKIM KRISTINA REED
OSNAT SHURER CLARK SPENCER

Executive Administrative Support

PATTI CONKLIN HEATHER FENG-YANU
MICHELLE MORETTA LIGHTNER TANYA OSKANIAN
BONNIE POPP TERRI SHEVY
WENDY DALE TANZILLO

Production Support & Artist Management

MEI-MING CASINO

VICKI CASE JEREMY COSTELLO
JACQUELYN GOLOMB-PEREZ KELLIE HOOVER
SHELLEY KATAYAMA COLLIN LARKINS
MELISSA ROBERTS

Development

MAGGIE MALONE
KAREN TENKHOFF
BRYAN DAVIDSON
ELISE ALIBERTI KELLY EISERT
KYLE GABRIEL KARA RAMOS
NICHOLAS RUSSELL SAM STRATTON
FELICITY TREVIÑO

Marketing & Publicity

AMY ASTLEY DAVID BESS
JOE DUNN HOWARD GREEN
MIKE GORTZ AMY KREUTZEN
TIA MELL DAVID SAMETH
MICHAEL SIMMS KYLE ZABALA

Business & Legal Affairs

CHRISTINE CHRISMAN
DOUG BRUNSWICK EDWIN KHANBEIGI
GUS AVILA JERI HOWARD
TIM GREER

Finance

JULIANNE HALE
DIRAN BANDAZIAN ROWENA Y. BARCELONA-NUQUI
TOM BODY CHRISTINA W. CHEN
DANIEL FEINER FRANK WILLIAM KNITTEL JR.
LINDA MATSUOKA-NARMORE ANGELA M. SABETTA

Environment & Events

TANJA KNOBLICH
CARLOS AREVALO REY CERVANTES JR.
DANIEL COSGROVE BENNY DeFRANCO
GARY DENES MELISSA COLE FANFASSIAN
KEN LEWIS BRUCE PARKER
EDUARDO RUIZ KEVIN WALDVOGEL-DeMONACO

Human Resources

KIM COSTELLO
DENISE IRWIN STASTNY HILDE VAN GOOL
GINGER WEI-HSIEN CHEN KATHERINE QUINTERO

Talent Development & Recruiting

DAWN RIVERA-ERNSTER
ANNIE BUHR SCOTT CAMPBELL
CAMILLE EDEN STEPHANIE MORSE
ROBYN PALMER MATT ROBERTS
KELSI TAGLANG ZULEMA URIARTE
DOERI WELCH GREINER

Training

TRACY BOVASSO CAMPBELL
ROSS BLOCHER CHRIS CHAVEZ
NANCY EVANS

Digital Art Services KENT GORDON

Caffeination CARLOS BENAVIDES

Special Projects

DAVID A. BOSSERT
ASHLEIGH BATEMAN BRANDON BLOCH
DAVID BLOCK MINNIE CHEN
LIANE ABEL DIETZ DARIN HOLLINGS
LURELINE KOHLER CAMERON RAMSAY

Animation Research Library

LELLA F. SMITH
MARY WALSH
JILL BREZNICAN FOX F. CARNEY
TAMMY CROSSON MARK M. DAWSON
DOUG ENGALLA IDRIS ERBA
MAT FRETSCHEL ANN W. HANSEN
LEON INGRAM RICHARD N. KANNO
TAMARA N. KHALAF TRACY ANN LEACH
MARISA LEONARDI KRISTEN McCORMICK
HEATHER McLAUGHLIN JAMIE PANETTA
TOM PNIEWSKI MIKE PUCHER
JACKIE VASQUEZ ELDA "TITA" VENEGAS
PATRICK WHITE

Ink & Paint

RIKKI CHOBANIAN JIM LUSBY
PEGGY MURAKAMI ANTONIO PELAYO
SHERRI VANDOLI

Consumer Products

MARY RENNER BEECH EMMANUEL DOESSANT
RENATO LATTANZI

Security

NORMAN GREEN MICHELLE HOWARD
FORREST IWASZEWSKI TERRY LA RAIA
ALAN MERCHANT JERRY ROMERO
DARRYL VONTOURE

In Memoriam

POPPY, LOLA, CALEB, KAYLA

The filmmakers would like to thank the Disney Story Trust and the Pixar Braintrust for their invaluable contribution, and the entire Disney Animation Studios for their dedication, support, ingenuity, and good humor.

SPECIAL THANKS

DR. KARL BIRKELAND
DR. JEFF DOZIER
THEIS DUELAND JENSEN
WARNER LOUGHLIN

JACKSON CRAWFORD
MICHAEL GOI, ASC
DIANA KURIYAMA
CRAIG SCHROEDER

DANILO
DAVID GOLDSTEIN
DR. KENNETH LIBBRECHT
JOSEPH M. TERAN

EINAR AASEN
LEROY BECKER
TRACY FARHAD
MAGNE EGGEN HAUGOM
LESLIE JAMES
MICHAEL KASCHALK
RICK MARZULLO
ELLING NIDENG
DR. THOMAS "DR. SNOW" PAINTER
LYNWOOD ROBINSON
THOMAS V. THOMPSON II

CYNTHIA BALLARDO
BJØRG BJØBERG
BRIAN GALE
JAMES P. HURRELL
RUNE JOHANSEN
KENNETH KENYON
KARL MJELVA
EVA NORDFJELL
BEATE ALBRIGTSEN PEDERSEN
SAGE THE REINDEER
ØYSTEIN USTVEDT

CLAUDIA BATCKE
INGER CARTER
THOMAS GRANDE
ESTHER JACOBSEN BATES
STINE ELISABETH JOHANSEN
KURT OVE LIDAL
ANNEKRISTIN MOE
ROSANNA PADOIN
GUNHILD REINSKOU
GEORGE STUART
BRIAN WHERRY

PHIL'S ANIMAL RENTALS
THE SCIENCE & ENTERTAINMENT EXCHANGE

PRODUCTION BABIES

ALEXANDRA	ÁLVARO	ANNIKA	ARDEN "HA-YEON"	ASHER
BRIAR	CALEB	CHARLOTTE	CLARA	CODY
ELIAS	EVERETT	EVEY	HIKARI	IVY
JEREMY	JOLIANNA	JULIAN	LIAM	LINCOLN
LUKE	NATHAN	NATHANIEL	OLIVER	OLIVER
PERI	PETRA	PROSPER	ROMAN	SARAH
SLOANE	THOMAS		TROUPE	WEDNESDAY

The views and opinions expressed by Kristoff in the film that all men eat their own boogers are solely his own and do not necessarily reflect the views or opinions of The Walt Disney Company or the filmmakers. Neither The Walt Disney Company nor the filmmakers make any representation of the accuracy of any such views and opinions.

Original Soundtrack Available on

Video Games Available From

Prints by DELUXE®

Distributed by
WALT DISNEY STUDIOS MOTION PICTURES